The T.O.P.* Workbook
For Taming Violence and Sexual Aggression

*Trauma Outcome Process

Joann Schladale, M.S., L.M.F.T.

Joann Schladale is a licensed marriage and family therapist who has been helping families heal from violence and sexual abuse for over twenty years. In addition to working with adjudicated youth Ms. Schladale provides training, consultation and clinical supervision for treatment providers in the United States, Canada, England and Russia.

Dedication

This workbook is lovingly dedicated to my brother, John, who suffered 25 stab wounds at the hand of a fifteen-year-old stranger on November 29, 1999.

Special Thanks

Special thanks are given to Alan Jenkins and Lucinda Rasmussen whose work revolutionized my way of thinking clinically.

I would also like to thank the dedicated state workers in Kentucky who made up the 1993 task force that adapted the trauma outcome process for clinical use.

They are
Randy Barnett, Kellie Landaker, Marcia Lane, JoAnn Lenahan, Libby Mills, and Jim Schorch.

Other kindred spirits who have enhanced the quality of this effort include
Brian Bill, David Braccialarghe, C.A. Brown, David Brown, Paul Castaldi, Joan Jurich and David Prescott.

My best friend Penny Howard provides great fun in our lives!

And, most importantly, the love and support of John and Canaan sustains me throughout the creative process.

Text copyright © 2002 by Joann Schladale

All rights reserved. No part of this book may be reproduced or transmitted in any form or by any means, electronic or mechanical, including photocopying, recording, or by any information storage and retrieving system, without written permission from the author.

Design by DeLucca Graphic Design, RI
Art Direction and Design by Sharon DeLucca
Typography by Donna Plasson
Illustration by Tyler Nevins

Printed by Signature Printing, RI

ISBN 0-9721401-0-7

To order copies of this workbook you can contact Ms. Schladale at:

Resources for Resolving Violence
28 Marshview Drive, Freeport, Maine 04032
207-865-3111
schladale@aol.com

Preface for Treatment Providers

Thank you for providing this workbook to support young men in their efforts to stop violent and sexually abusive behavior. The purpose of The T.O.P.* Workbook for Taming Violence and Sexual Aggression is to help young people make sense of pain in their lives that has influenced decisions to commit criminal acts. Research on this topic indicates that sequential patterns of destructive behavior can be identified and stopped. Aggressive responses can be tamed and turned into coping strategies that enhance possibilities for successful treatment outcomes. This workbook is designed to do just that.

The T.O.P.* Workbook was created to provide a structured approach for exploring the impact of previous trauma on destructive behavior. The Trauma Outcome Process is a conceptual framework created by Lucinda Rasmussen Ph.D. who writes extensively on the topic. This workbook represents an integration of clinical material relating to trauma, violence and sexual aggression from a variety of sources and professional disciplines. Some of these resources are listed in the back of the workbook. It is designed for young men and their family members to use collaboratively with staff trained in providing a therapeutic response to aggressive behavior.

This is a workbook that can be used throughout the full continuum of care in both community-based and residential settings. Accountability and responsibility for criminal behavior are paramount in treatment. Only recently have broader issues relating to the context of aggressive behavior been identified and acknowledged to be important components of relapse prevention. The content can be integrated and used in conjunction with other treatment materials. Many programs utilize a variety of resource materials to stop problematic behavior. This workbook is designed to enhance, rather than exclude, the use of a broad range of material resources that can support the efforts of these young men.

The T.O.P.* Workbook explores a great deal of sensitive information and should be facilitated with ongoing support and consistent interaction. Research indicates that therapeutic change, and healing, occurs within the context of a therapeutic relationship. Adolescents left alone to figure out such complex experiences may struggle in isolation. Collaboration with trusted others might prevent unnecessary replication of painful experiences that place them at risk of reoffense. Youth should not be required to share sensitive information from the workbook in settings that can make feelings of vulnerability worse. Thoughtful clinical preparation, informed consent, and therapeutic collaboration with each youth, should be used before addressing workbook topics in group and/or family therapy.

Workbook activities may lead some participants to reveal previously unreported criminal acts. They may be crimes that the youth committed, crimes that were perpetrated against them, or crimes that they witnessed or heard about. Addressing all aspects of confidentiality prior to using the workbook can eliminate potential problems that might arise from misunderstandings about a treatment provider's duty to report, even the suspicion of, criminal behavior. This workbook provides a context for honoring such revelations as acts of courage that represent important steps in the healing process.

Table of Contents

Introduction to the Trauma Outcome Process

Welcome to the T.O.P.* Workbook for Taming Violence and Sexual Aggression. T.O.P.* stands for Trauma Outcome Process. *Trauma means bad things that have a lasting effect on your life. Outcome is a result, or consequence. A process is a particular way of doing something.* Your trauma outcome process is the way you choose to deal with bad things that have happened to you. *Tame means to change, control or overcome fierceness or wildness. Violence is any physical force used to hurt, damage, or destroy.* It is also an unfair use of power. *Sexual refers to anything involving sex* and *aggression is any forceful, attacking behavior.* So sexual aggression is anytime sex is used to hurt someone. You can learn to take control of violence, or sexual aggression, and tame it. You can get it out of your life! And get on with your life!

These words will be explained in a lot more detail throughout the book. Right now you can get started by just reading a bit to help you get comfortable with the information.

Top 10
REASONS FOR THIS WORKBOOK

1. To help you tame violence and sexual aggression!

2. To explore getting into trouble versus staying out of trouble!

3. To learn how to manage problems without causing harm to yourself and/or others

4. To reduce confusion and ease pain in your life

5. To make your life, and treatment, easier

6. To learn how to take good care of yourself

7. To connect with people you can trust

8. To help you focus on your dreams!

9. To explore becoming the person you really want to be!

10. To have a lot more fun in your life!

1

chapter one: Getting Into Trouble Versus Staying Out of Trouble

This book was created for a variety of reasons. The most important reasons are to help you tame aggressive behavior. When you struggle with getting into trouble versus staying out of trouble there is a possibility that you'll end up in jail. Aggressive behavior can prevent you from becoming the person you really want to be. It can get in the way of your dreams! Getting into trouble gets in the way of having fun and enjoying life! This book provides an opportunity to change your way of thinking about aggression and to stop it.

You might be wondering why you should bother with this workbook. Some young people who have gotten into trouble don't see any point in staying out of trouble. Getting into trouble can serve a purpose. It can get other people's attention. It can make others afraid of you. You might think it will make people leave you alone. It might even be sensational and invite media attention. You might not believe that anything can change to make things better in your life. You might believe that ignoring the pain in your life will make it go away. You might also think that people wanting to help have nothing of value to say to you.

Struggling with getting into trouble versus staying out of trouble is hard! You may have a lot of confusion about the things that have gotten you into trouble. There are pros and cons to consider staying out of trouble. You may feel like you have to give up some things you don't want to when you decide to stay out of trouble. There will be a lot of difficult decisions to make along the way. They are decisions that only you can make. No one can force you to make them. Take your time to think about the different things that play a part in getting into trouble versus staying out of trouble.

Curtis was a smart young man who was upset about a lot of things in his life. He was sexually abusing his younger brothers and being cruel to the family dog. He even attempted to explode a hand-made bomb. Curtis was getting a lot of attention from investigators and treatment providers but not the love and attention he needed and wanted from his parents. He said he didn't want to continue doing those things but he didn't know how to stop. Curtis realized that he really wanted to learn how to have a girlfriend and to talk to his parents about how badly they were treating him. He was able to share his frustration with adults who understood his problems and who helped him to think about other ways to solve them. He dared to take a stand for himself and began to think about ways of staying out of trouble.

By learning to change your behavior you can stop getting into trouble and focus on becoming the person that you really want to be. When you are able to manage problems without causing harm to yourself, or others, you have a lot more time to focus on your dreams. Consider learning how to follow your dreams. You can do it! Even when really bad things have happened hopes and dreams can survive. It may be very difficult but change is possible.

This workbook was also created to help make your life, and treatment, easier. Young people receive a lot of messages about aggressive behavior that cause confusion about getting into trouble versus staying out of trouble. Television shows and videos might make you think that violence and sexual aggression are cool. Seeing people act aggressively might make you think power like that is good to have. Power that comes from aggression is bad. Aggressive behavior causes a lot of confusion for a lot of people. This workbook can help reduce a lot of the confusion. The activities in this workbook have been created to help you figure out ways to ease the pain in your life. You can do this by slowing down and taking time to make sense out of all the confusion. This can be a big challenge!

Some of the young men who murdered people in their schools shared stories about feeling powerless in the face of bullies. They were treated badly by classmates and often felt isolated and alone. All of the violence they watched on television and reports about the other killings influenced their desires to go out in a blaze of glory. They got confused about what glory really is and ended up committing acts of shame and disgrace.

Top 10 REASONS FOR
STAYING OUT OF TROUBLE

1. FREEDOM!

2. SUCCESS!

3. ENJOYMENT!

4. AFFECTION!

5. LOVE!

6. POWER!

7. CONTROL!

8. MONEY!

9. GOOD FOOD!

10. FUN!

Top10
WAYS PEOPLE CAN HELP YOU

1. They can listen to you

2. They can help you with your work

3. They can have fun with you

4. They can provide spiritual guidance

5. They can get to know you

6. They can talk with you

7. They can coach you

8. They can share wisdom

9. They can teach you

10. They can comfort you

When bad things happen it's often very hard to make sense of them. When adults aren't there to help, children often struggle with things alone. Some kids who have gotten into trouble stay away from others and spend a lot of time alone. Sometimes being alone is good and helps people calm down. Too much time alone can make you feel lonely, and sometimes, scared. It might also make you think that nobody cares and that there's nobody you can trust. You might not believe it but there are people who are trustworthy. Making sense of getting into trouble can help you figure out a lot of things about how to stay out of trouble. It can help you learn about people you can trust and those people you cannot trust. It can help you learn how to enjoy being with people who help you feel good about yourself and avoid those who cause pain. It can help you learn how to have a lot more fun in your life!

Connection

Connecting with other people is one of the most important things you do in life. When you consider getting into trouble versus staying out of trouble there are a lot of things to think about. You can't do it alone. A lot of people can help you. Others can support you in many ways. You may want to have someone with you as you answer questions throughout the workbook. You may want to work alone sometimes and meet with others to talk about the answers. You may want to share your doubts about the value of this workbook with

Patrick never talked about anything personal to anyone. He didn't see any point in talking. He was in a correctional facility for almost a year after his arrest before he considered telling staff about his problems. When he finally did it terrified him. In an effort to cover up his fear, he got into a physical fight with staff. It took him a long time to realize that staff was not there to hurt him and that he could tell his family what was going on without getting into more trouble.

As soon as Darrel could get hold of drugs or alcohol he began using them to block out the pain in his life. He saw his parents do the same thing so he thought it would work for him. What he didn't realize is that substance abuse doesn't work to heal pain. It just covers it up for the time being.

Darrel had never seen adults in his life taking good care of themselves so he didn't have any ideas about how to take good care of himself. He was used to people smoking, drinking, overeating, and doing dangerous things like fighting and driving recklessly. When he couldn't get any drugs or alcohol he learned how to manage his pain differently. He began to learn how people heal from painful experiences by daring to give up bad habits. He took the risk to feel the pain so that he could figure out where it was coming from and how to begin a search for solutions. Unfortunately, others in his family were not successful. His mother died from alcohol related problems but Darrel continues to try to take good care of himself.

someone who will listen to you. Talking with others can help you figure out exactly how the answers to all of the questions will help you make sense of getting into trouble versus staying out of trouble. These answers will help you decide how to tame violence and sexually aggressive behavior.

This workbook can also help you to learn how to take good care of yourself. *Taking good care of yourself means protecting yourself, and others from harm.* It is also a way to learn how to keep yourself out of trouble. This means learning to prevent bad things from happening to you. It also means making sure that you don't hurt yourself or others.

Tobi

You may be wondering why you should bother taking good care of yourself. You might also find yourself wondering why adults in your life may not have taken better care of you. These are questions that come up all the time in life. They're hard questions and sometimes you might not want to be bothered by them. This is part of the challenge of getting into trouble versus staying out of trouble. When you consider taking good care of yourself think about how it might help you. You might also want to think about ways that taking care of yourself can be scary, or threatening.

TOP 10 WAYS YOU CAN TAKE GOOD CARE OF YOURSELF!

1. Laugh as much as possible

2. Don't smoke, or abuse substances

3. Cry when you need to

4. Love

5. Make good friends

6. Relax

7. Speak your truth respectfully

8. Meditate

9. Exercise

10. Have fun!

Change

All human beings are constantly changing. Yet while we are changing there are some things that feel like they remain the same. As you've grown up you may have noticed that you are good at something like schoolwork, art, or sports. Since you've gotten into trouble, you might think that nobody notices good things that you do. So if you've tried to change some things but others keep giving you messages that you're bad, it can be frustrating. You might be thinking, what's the point? You might feel like you don't want to change, or you may be afraid of change. When you find that there are things you don't like about yourself you may want to consider change. Sometimes you may feel like you don't have the power to make things change. You do!

When you think about the reasons for this work book, reasons for struggling with getting into trouble versus staying out of trouble, and reasons for wanting to take good care of yourself, they're all about change. This whole book is about change. Take your time to think about change. The more you think about it the more likely you will be to make good and lasting changes. It might also help you to think more clearly about some dreams you have.

Practice

This workbook has a lot of questions! The only way you can become the person you want to be is to figure out answers to many questions that come up in life. This takes practice. You may notice that a lot of the questions are alike. This is so that you can successfully learn how to tame violence and sexual aggression.

Thomas was a young man with mental retardation and a mental illness that caused him a lot of anger and frustration. He dreamed of graduating from high school and living on his own but his violence and sexual aggression landed him in residential treatment. While he was there he was able to get medication for his illness and he was able to think about how he might correct the mistakes he had made. He was not allowed to return to his old school so he studied to get his diploma while he was in treatment. He created a plan to get a place of his own when he was discharged and he shared the plan with his family. When he returned home he was offered a job at a local discount store and began to put the plan into place.

The practice it takes to become the person you want to be is just like the practice it takes a baseball team to win the World Series. Every question you answer is like making a good catch or hitting the ball when you're at bat. It gives you practice to keep making more good catches and hitting more balls. Everybody who gets up to bat strikes out sometimes. All good catchers drop the ball sometimes. All players experience a slump in their performance when things just aren't going well for them. This is like the challenge of getting into trouble versus staying out of trouble. It takes constant practice that involves some home runs and some strike outs.

When you get to be a really good player you get to go to the major leagues. When you excel in the majors, you become an all star and are recruited by the best teams. Even the most valuable players practice doing their best all the time! When you feel like a winner, you want to keep winning!

Now, you may never play baseball, but you can still be a winner! You can win in the world series of life by making sense of how you have been getting into trouble and practicing ways to stay out of trouble. You can take good care of yourself and create a plan to make your dreams come true. You can become the person you want to be.

When you are clear about your dreams and how to accomplish them, you will understand how the questions in this book are practice for becoming the person you want to be. When you find questions frustrating, scary or boring, talk to someone about them. You might ask someone to tell you how a troubling question can help you.

Getting Into Trouble Versus Staying Out of Trouble

Why should I bother thinking about getting into trouble versus staying out of trouble?

_____

_____

What's the point of staying out of trouble?

_____

_____

Who cares whether I get into trouble or stay out of trouble?

_____

_____

What good will it do me to stay out of trouble?

_____

_____

Why might I want to change anything about myself?

_____

_____

Who might I look up to as a model for staying out of trouble?

_____

_____

When am I successful at staying out of trouble?

_____

_____

Dreams

Everybody has dreams. I'm not talking about dreams that you have when you're sleeping. I'm talking about fond hopes and desires that everyone thinks about. These may be dreams about what you want to do when you grow up. They may be about where you want to live and who you want to live with. They might be about wanting to go to school to study something that you are interested in. Dreams involve thinking about the type of person you want to become.

Teenage years are a good time to begin thinking about hopes and dreams so that you can start preparing now to become the person you want to be. Sometimes dreams feel scary because you may not believe that you can achieve a certain dream. Sometimes people give up on their dreams or talk themselves out of their dreams. It's important to know what your dreams are. When you are able to think clearly about your dreams, and let others know about them, you can often achieve them.

Dreams

Why should I bother thinking about any hopes and dreams I have for myself?

_____

What things get in the way of following my dreams?

_____

How can I take a stand to make my dreams come true?

_____

Who comes to mind when I think of someone who has struggled and made their dreams come true?

_____

When am I successfully working towards any of my dreams?

_____

_____

Top 10 DREAMS I HAVE FOR MYSELF

_____

_____

_____

_____

_____

_____

_____

_____

_____

Courage

Courage means being able to deal with anything that's difficult. *Courage is the attitude of facing and dealing with anything recognized as dangerous, difficult, or painful, instead of withdrawing from it.* Your courage can help you find the strength to tackle trouble. The more you practice being courageous the better you get at it!

Getting into trouble involved acting in response to pain and fear in ways that led to dishonesty and crime. Staying out of trouble requires courage and strength. It requires thinking about things differently than you have in the past. This book can help you find courage and strength to learn about yourself and to stop getting into trouble.

Courage

How does courage play a part in getting into trouble versus staying out of trouble?

_____

_____

When am I courageous?

_____

_____

What helps me to be courageous?

_____

_____

Who comes to mind when I think of a courageous person?

_____

_____

How do they show their courage?

_____

_____

How can I use what I know about courage to consider a successful change in my life?

_____

_____

Top 10
IMPORTANT THINGS ABOUT COURAGE

_____

_____

_____

_____

_____

_____

_____

_____

_____

_____

Strength

Strength is having the power to get something done. Strength is not just about the power your muscles have to lift or move something. Strength also involves making a decision to do something and sticking with it. Strength is knowing what is right and doing it. Strength is about taking a stand for something you believe in, even when you are the only one willing to do so. Strength requires hard work.

It takes great strength to stay out of trouble. Using strength to face trouble can help you to stop causing harm. Strength helps you to stand tall and talk about trouble honestly. When you are able to tackle trouble you become stronger than it is. When you are confident in having the courage and strength to tackle trouble you are able to tame physical and sexual aggression.

Strength

How does strength play a part in getting into trouble versus staying out of trouble?

_____

_____

When do I successfully use my strength?

_____

_____

What helps me to be strong?

_____

_____

Who comes to mind when I think of a strong person?

_____

_____

How do they show their strength?

_____

_____

How can I use what I know about strength to consider a successful change in my life?

_____

_____

Top 10
IMPORTANT THINGS ABOUT STRENGTH

_____

_____

_____

_____

_____

_____

_____

_____

_____

_____

Respect

Taming violence and sexual aggression requires respect. *Respect means showing consideration*. It is having concern for you and for all other living things. Respect is treating everyone and everything with kindness and regard for well being. When you genuinely care for yourself and others you no longer have a desire to cause hurt and pain. That doesn't mean you won't feel angry and frustrated at times. Everyone feels angry at times. It just means that when you do feel angry you can learn to resolve anger in ways that no longer cause harm to yourself, or anyone else. You can learn to manage your anger with respect.

When children have not been treated with respect it is hard for them to learn how to treat others that way. It may take a lot of practice. These questions are just a beginning for learning about respect and how it can help you throughout your life.

Respect

How does respect play a part in getting into trouble versus staying out of trouble?

_____

_____

When do I feel respected?

_____

_____

When am I being respectful towards others?

_____

_____

Who comes to mind when I think of a respectful person?

_____

_____

How do they show respect?

_____

_____

How can I use what I know about respect to consider a successful change in my life?

_____

_____

_____

_____

Conclusion

This concludes the introduction to this workbook. Making decisions about getting into trouble versus staying out of trouble are very challenging. Such decisions take a lot of thought and practice. You will have an opportunity to explore getting into trouble versus staying out of trouble as you complete the following chapters. Each section is intended to help you think about yourself and your actions so that you can tame violence and sexual aggression. Each question was created to help you become the person you want to be and pursue your dreams. You can consider doing this without causing harm to yourself or others. Everyone is faced with many temptations to get into trouble. Staying out of trouble requires taking a stand against such temptations.

It takes courage and strength to believe in yourself, especially when others may doubt you. It also takes a lot of practice to be patient with all of the questions that are coming. Figuring out all this stuff can be quite a challenge. Making a decision to stay out of trouble is hard. Daring to take a stand for yourself can be scary. Thinking about getting into trouble versus staying out of trouble is not for the faint-hearted. It is a personal decision, not one that can be imposed by others. Only you can decide what is really in your best interest.

Please remember to take your time, and give yourself a break when it feels too hard. Taking your time helps you to learn how to take good care of yourself. You can relax a bit in order to gain some energy to move on. If you find that you are avoiding questions because they stir up troublesome thoughts think about how you will find the courage to tell someone you trust so that they can help you along the way. You're not in this alone and there are people around you who really want to help.

REFLECTIONS ON GETTING INTO TROUBLE VERSUS STAYING OUT OF TROUBLE

How willing am I to think about getting into trouble versus staying out of trouble?

_____

_____

What parts of getting into trouble is it hard to let go of?

_____

_____

What are some of my reasons for wanting to stay out of trouble?

_____

_____

When am I successful at staying out of trouble?

_____

_____

Who helps me to stay out of trouble?

_____

_____

How ready am I to take a stand for myself and consider following my dreams?

_____

_____

What will help me prepare to go on to the next section of the workbook?

_____

_____

The purpose of this chapter is to help you take a look at your life and think about choices that you make. This workbook is about a variety of life experiences. Looking at different parts of your life can help you to learn more about how you act and decisions you make about getting into trouble versus staying out of trouble. Answering the questions is an opportunity for you to think about yourself and the things in your life that influence you. The answers can help you consider change by learning about the best ways to take care of yourself. They can help you tame violence and sexual aggression and help you to be clear about the person you want to be.

My Self

How you think about yourself influences how you act. When you like yourself and assume that others will like you too, you are more likely to be friendly and enjoy being around others who feel the same way. If people have said bad things about you, or treated you badly, you may incorrectly think that you are bad. You may also incorrectly think that all people are bad. All human beings are very complicated. No one is just bad or good. Even when people have done bad things it does not mean that they are all bad.

Take some time to think about yourself so that you can better understand how all the different parts come together to make you who you are. How you think about yourself can be influenced by how you think others see you. Pay attention to those things you like best about yourself. Think about parts of yourself that you might not be too happy with right now. How you see yourself influences getting into trouble versus staying out of trouble. Take time to think about how you want people to see you. This will give you ideas about how you might want to change. It can also give you information that will help you tame violence and sexual aggression.

chapter two: My Life Experiences

My Self

How do thoughts about myself influence getting into trouble versus staying out of trouble?

_____

_____

What have been the biggest influences on how I think about myself?

_____

_____

What am I learning about myself now?

_____

_____

What challenges am I facing about myself?

_____

_____

How is this new information helping me to find courage, strength and respect?

_____

_____

How can I use what I know about myself to make a successful change in my life?

_____

_____

Top 10
IMPORTANT THINGS ABOUT ME

_____

_____

_____

_____

_____

_____

_____

_____

_____

_____

Sex

Sex is a big part of everyone's life. Sex is a whole lot of things and it can be very confusing! A person's sex tells us whether they are, female or male. Sex is also anything connected with sexual pleasure. The word sex is often used to describe the act of sexual intercourse and reproduction. Reproduction is the process by which humans, animals and plants create new individuals.

Sex is a part of everyone's development and it effects how you think and feel about yourself and others. Since it plays such a big part in life, this workbook focuses a lot on sex. When people confuse sex with love and affection it causes problems. Such confusion can play a part in decisions to commit acts of violence and sexual aggression. It is important to clear up any misunderstandings so that it doesn't cause these kinds of problems.

Sex-Roles

Boys and girls get a lot of messages about sex. Just like love, and many other things in this workbook, sex can be really confusing. Some people think you are supposed to act a certain way if you are male or female. You may have received messages to "stand tall and be a man". This might mean you should be honest and proud to hold your head high because of the good things you do. It can also be mistaken as permission to bully others. A lot of boys think you have to be tough to be a man.

Boys often get messages that you are supposed to act a certain way in order to become a "real" man. To be "cool" you might get pressure to hide your emotions, act fearless and pretend to always be in control. These types of messages are called sex-role messages, or gender messages. They are called this because they give you ideas about your "role" as a male. *Gender indicates your membership in a group of males*. Girls also get gender messages about their sex-roles as women.

Some messages make it hard to be genuine. Genuine means really being you. It is being sincere and honest and true. Everybody has strong emotions at one time or another. Everybody gets scared at times and nobody is in control of things all the time. Take some time to figure out messages you have received that influence your ideas about manhood. It can help you to make sense of them and decide what you want to do with them. You will have an opportunity to think about which ones you want to keep and which ones you want to consider getting rid of.

Gender Messages I Got About Sex-Roles

How do messages about men and women influence getting into trouble versus staying out of trouble?

_____

_____

What have been the biggest influences on how I think about men's and women's roles?

_____

_____

What am I learning about these messages now?

_____

_____

What challenges am I facing about what I think about men's and women's roles?

_____

_____

How is this new information helping me to find courage, strength and respect?

_____

_____

How can I use what I know about these messages to make a successful change in my life?

_____

_____

Top 10
IMPORTANT THINGS ABOUT SEX-ROLES

_____

_____

_____

_____

_____

_____

_____

_____

_____

_____

Sexual Arousal

Sexual stimulation, or arousal, is a body's physical response to something that triggers sexual feelings. Stimulation, or arousal, occurs when you feel excited about something. In this case it is when your body feels something that makes you experience excitement relating to your genitals. There are a lot of things that make you feel sexually aroused. Exploring some of those things can help you to understand how your body responds sexually to a variety of things.

Sexual arousal can be involved in violence and sexual aggression. Since aggression is forceful, attacking behavior, it is hurtful. Exploring your feelings about sexual arousal can help you make sense of some confusion you may have about it. It can help you to better understand sexual aggression. When you know a lot about sexual aggression you can tame it. When you successfully tame sexual aggression you can learn to experience sexual pleasure in ways that no longer causes harm to yourself or others.

Sexual arousal can be fun! It is something all human beings experience and it can be managed in a variety of different ways. Everyone feels sexually aroused at times when it is not appropriate to engage in sexual acts. Everyone is challenged to learn how to manage sexual arousal without having orgasm, or intercourse, and without causing harm to anyone.

Lots of teenagers engage in flirtation as a way of experiencing sexual arousal and sexual pleasure. *Flirtation is playing at love. It is kind and considerate attention given to someone you are sexually attracted to.* It might involve activities like good-natured joking, smiling, playing games, or dancing.

Some people confuse flirtation with teasing but they are different. *Teasing is annoying, or harassing by mocking or poking fun.* Sexual teasing can hurt people's feelings. It can be a type of sexual harassment, which is against the law.

When you find yourself becoming sexually aroused you have a lot of choices about how to handle your arousal. You can ignore it until it goes away. If you are alone in a private place you may chose to masturbate. Masturbation is handling your own genitals for the purpose of sexual pleasure. If you are with a consenting partner you may engage in flirtation and other things like holding hands, hugging each other, or kissing. It is important to make sure that participating in any of these activities is okay with your partner.

Sexual Arousal

How does sexual arousal play a part in getting into trouble versus staying out of trouble?

_____

_____

What have been the biggest influences on how I experience sexual arousal?

_____

_____

What am I learning about sexual arousal now?

_____

_____

What challenges am I facing about sexual arousal?

_____

_____

How is this new information helping me to find courage, strength and respect?

_____

_____

How can I use what I know about sexual arousal to make a successful change in my life?

_____

_____

Top 10 WAYS I CAN EXPERIENCE SEXUAL AROUSAL WITHOUT CAUSING HARM

_____

_____

_____

_____

_____

_____

_____

_____

_____

_____

Sexual Pleasure

Sexual pleasure is anything that our body finds to be sexually enjoyable, delightful and satisfying. *Sexual pleasure involves sexual stimulation that does not include any pain or bad experiences.*

Learning the difference between sexual arousal and sexual pleasure can help you understand yourself better. Sexual pleasure involves intimate enjoyment of your body. Intimate means private or personal. It also means very close. Sexual pleasure may include sexual intimacy with another person who clearly agrees to share in the pleasure. It involves giving and receiving sexual stimulation that does not cause harm to yourself or your partner. Sexual pleasure is not hurtful in any way.

Sexual Pleasure

How does sexual pleasure play a part in getting into trouble versus staying out of trouble?

_____

_____

What have been the biggest influences on how I experience sexual pleasure?

_____

_____

What am I learning about sexual pleasure now?

_____

_____

What challenges am I facing about sexual pleasure?

_____

_____

How is this new information helping me to find courage, strength and respect?

_____

_____

How can I use what I know about sexual pleasure to make a successful change in my life?

_____

_____

Top 10 IMPORTANT THINGS
ABOUT EXPERIENCING SEXUAL PLEASURE

_____

_____

_____

_____

_____

_____

_____

_____

_____

_____

Sexual Intercourse

Sexual intercourse is the sexual joining of two individuals. Even though sex refers to many different things, a lot of people think of sexual intercourse whenever the topic of sex comes up. Sexual intercourse is just one way of engaging in sexual behavior. The act of sexual intercourse usually refers to a man putting his penis into a woman's vagina. Sexual intercourse can also occur between two males, or two females. Males might use their anus, or other body parts, to receive the penis, and females can use their hands, or other body parts, to sexually stimulate a partner's vagina. Sexual intercourse can involve a variety of sexual behavior.

The ways in which a person learns about sexual intercourse can influence thoughts, feelings and actions about sexuality. Exploring these experiences can help you to make sense of the ways that you behave sexually. It can help you to make connections between your early learning and the ways that you express your sexuality now. It can also help you to consider things that you might want to change about your sexual expression.

Sexual Intercourse

How does sexual intercourse play a part in getting into trouble versus staying out of trouble?

_____

_____

What have been the biggest influences on how I think about sexual intercourse?

_____

_____

What am I learning about sexual intercourse now?

_____

_____

What challenges am I facing about sexual intercourse?

_____

_____

How is this new information helping me to find courage, strength and respect?

_____

_____

How can I use what I know about sexual intercourse to make a successful change in my life?

_____

_____

Top 10 IMPORTANT
THINGS ABOUT SEXUAL INTERCOURSE

_____

_____

_____

_____

_____

_____

_____

_____

Love

Love is a deep and tender feeling of attachment. It is a very powerful emotion that influences our behavior. Human beings seek love and affection naturally. Affection is fond or tender feeling. Love is a wonderful experience when it reflects genuine care, concern and respect. Love and affection do not necessarily go together. Sometimes people feel love and do not express it through affectionate behavior. Sometimes it is hard for people to show love through tender acts of kindness and respect. Love can be very confusing. It can be hard to understand that someone loves you when they treat you badly. People who do that are confused about love. Their actions show their confusion and pain.

It takes courage to express love with tender affection. It takes strength to openly receive love. Love can make some people feel vulnerable. *Vulnerable means open to being wounded or easily hurt*. When children are hurt by people who are supposed to love them, they can feel vulnerable and become afraid of love. Developing the courage and strength to love with tender affection takes practice. It takes courage to face the fear of being hurt and learn that broken hearts can be mended. Strong hearts can be hurt and go on to love again. A courageous and strong heart just keeps on loving and caring even when times are tough and bad things happen.

Love

How does love play a part in getting into trouble versus staying out of trouble?

_____

_____

What have been the biggest influences on how I experience love?

_____

_____

What am I learning about love now?

_____

_____

What challenges am I facing about love?

_____

_____

How is this new information helping me to find courage, strength and respect?

_____

_____

How can I use what I know about love to make a successful change in my life?

_____

_____

Top 10 IMPORTANT THINGS ABOUT LOVE

_____

_____

_____

_____

_____

_____

_____

_____

_____

My Family

Families play a big part in everyone's life. They greatly influence your life experiences. Where you grow up, who you grow up with, how family members act, and what family's value, all play a part in helping you to understand yourself. Exploring different things about your family can help you to learn more about how you have learned to handle yourself in different situations.

My Family

How has my family played a part in my getting into trouble versus staying out of trouble?

_____

_____

What have been the biggest influences on how I think about my family?

_____

_____

What am I learning about my family now?

_____

_____

What challenges am I facing about my family?

_____

_____

How is this new information helping me to find courage, strength and respect?

_____

_____

How can I use what I know about my family to make a successful change in my life?

_____

_____

Top 10
IMPORTANT THINGS ABOUT MY FAMILY

_____

_____

_____

_____

_____

_____

_____

_____

_____

_____

My School

How does school play a part in getting into trouble versus staying out of trouble?

_____

_____

What have been the biggest influences on how I experience school?

_____

_____

What am I learning about school now?

_____

_____

What challenges am I facing about school?

_____

_____

How is this new information helping me to find courage, strength and respect?

_____

_____

How can I use what I know about school to help make a successful change in my life?

_____

_____

My School

Most children spend a lot of time at school. Your thoughts about school play a big part in how well you perform in school and how much you learn. How well you learn different subjects and how you get along with others in school influences what other people, like teachers and other students, think about you. Lots of times, what others think of you influences how you think about yourself, and how you act. Because you spend so much time there, school can have a big impact on your life.

Answering questions about school can give you information about how you like to learn and what you are interested in learning. It can give you some ideas about how you like to work and what kind of work you like to do. Exploring the questions can help you think about your success in completing this workbook and treatment. It can help you clarify dreams and create new ones.

My Community

Community means the condition of living with others. Your community consists of all the people and places you come in contact with on a regular basis. The neighborhood you live in is your immediate community. Your school is a big part of your community. If you go to church, the church, and other people who go there, are a part of your community. Places you shop are also a part of your community. Places where you participate in activities like social events and sports are also a part of your community. Places where you and your family members work are important parts of your community. Even the streets are a part of your community. The community you grow up in has a big influence on your life.

My Community

How does my community play a part in my getting into trouble versus staying out of trouble?

_____

_____

What have been the biggest influences on how I experience my community?

_____

_____

What am I learning about my community now?

_____

_____

What challenges am I facing about my community?

_____

_____

How is this new information helping me to find courage, strength and respect?

_____

_____

How can I use my community to make a successful change in my life?

_____

_____

Friendship

How does friendship play a part in getting into trouble versus staying out of trouble?

_____

_____

What have been the biggest influences on how I have experienced friendship in my life?

_____

_____

What am I learning about friendship now?

_____

_____

What challenges am I facing about friendship?

_____

_____

How is this new information helping me to find courage, strength and respect?

_____

_____

How can I use what I know about friendship to make a successful change in my life?

_____

_____

Friendship

A friend is someone you like who provides support and is not an enemy. Friendships occur in a variety of situations and can change over time. When you are little friendship is mostly about playing together. As you get older, in addition to being a pal, friends can provide support and help you through tough times. Friends can help you to feel a deep sense of connection and belonging. Friendships can also become painful and end due to differences of opinion about things you like or dislike. Friends can also influence your life. Friends are not necessarily your own age. They can be younger, or older, male or female. Friendships can grow between any people regardless of differences. Friendship is based upon care and concern for another person.

Conclusion

You have just completed a lot of important work exploring a variety of life experiences. Congratulations on a job well done! Some people go through their whole life without making sense of how life experiences influence thoughts, feelings and actions. Finding the strength and courage to do so allows you to be thoughtful about what you want to do with this knowledge. You can consider what you want to take control of and change so that you can take good care of yourself, become the person you want to be, and pursue your dreams. Before you go any further you may want to review the work you have done so far and reflect on your accomplishments.

REFLECTIONS ON MY LIFE EXPERIENCES

How willing am I to think about how my life experiences play a part in getting into trouble versus staying out of trouble?

_____

_____

What parts of my life experiences are hard to face?

_____

_____

How can I use courage, strength and respect to face them?

_____

_____

How ready am I to take a stand for taming violence and sexual aggression?

_____

_____

What will help me prepare to go on to the next chapter of the workbook?

_____

_____

Top 10 IMPORTANT
THINGS ABOUT MY LIFE EXPERIENCES

_____

_____

_____

_____

_____

_____

_____

_____

_____

chapter three: Bad Things That Happen in Life

As children grow up, bad things sometimes happen. Bad things happen to everyone. Bad things that happened to you in the past can play a part in getting into trouble versus staying out of trouble. They can get in the way of taking good care of yourself and becoming the person you want to be.

In order to figure out answers you have to ask yourself a lot more questions. So get ready! It really takes a lot of questions for you to figure out the best ways to take good care of yourself. There are a lot of things that influenced your decision to act in violent and sexually aggressive ways, so it takes a lot of thinking to figure out the best ways to tame those behaviors. Don't worry though; you can take time to answer them. You can answer one or two at a time, or a whole section. It doesn't matter. What matters is that you take some time to think about all of this so that you can figure out how to take good care of yourself and stay out of trouble. Feel free to have someone you like help you with these questions.

Some of the questions may be hard to answer. They will bring up bad things that have happened to you. It can be scary to think about bad things that have happened. People often don't want to think about scary things and don't want to talk about scary things. It's extra scary if you tried to talk about some of these things before and nothing got better. Some kids may have tried to talk about difficult things and felt that it made matters worse. That's really awful!

It's important to be aware that you might feel vulnerable as you're figuring out the questions. A lot of young men are afraid of feeling vulnerable. Remember, Vulnerable means open to being wounded or easily hurt. While you may be afraid of someone putting you down because of the bad things that have happened to you, when you are in safe company that won't happen.

You might also feel shame as you think about these things. *Shame is a painful feeling of having lost the respect of others because of bad behavior.* Shame brings up thoughts about dishonor and disgrace. Some bad things that happen in life are shameful. Almost everyone has experiences that cause shame.

So it's okay to be scared to think about some of these things, it's okay to be scared to talk about them, and it's okay to feel shame about them. It takes courage, and strength, and people who make you feel safe, to be able to overcome this fear and shame. You can do it! Consider sharing your fears with someone you trust. It often helps people to feel better. A wise woman used to say that by sharing our pain it becomes less painful. She was right. But it's still scary.

When you are able to answer the questions you might be surprised by some of the feelings that you have. Many people report that they actually feel better after figuring out the answers to these questions. Some report that they feel lighter, as though a burden has been lifted off their shoulders. Others say that they understand things more clearly. Once you know the answers you will be able to consider new solutions to heal the pain. Healing pain without causing harm to yourself or others is a key to taming violence and sexual aggression.

Bad Things That Happen in Life

Sickness: When any part of your body suffers from an illness.

Moving: When you have to change the place where you live and you don't want to.

Loss: When someone, or something, you care about is no longer in your life.

Natural Disaster: When bad things happen in nature that cause harm. This might be a storm, or fire, that damages homes and hurts people.

Accident: Something unexpected that hurts people.

Poverty: Not having enough of things that you need.

Prejudice: Negative judgement about people that causes harm.

School Problems: Bad things that happen at school.

Social Problems: Bad things that happen when you're with other people.

Family Problems: Bad things that happen in your family.

Divorce: When parents decide that they don't want to be married any more and the family no longer lives together.

Neglect: When adults are not able to take care of children.

Verbal Abuse: When someone says hurtful things to you, or others that can cause you to feel badly about yourself.

Emotional Abuse: When someone hurts your feelings in a way that keeps you from being able to do things that you should be able to do as you are growing up.

Physical Abuse: When someone hurts your body and leaves marks of any kind. You might have to go to the doctor or hospital.

Sexual Abuse: When someone uses you for his or her own sexual needs. They might touch you on different parts of your body that includes your genitals. They might make you look at their genitals, or make you do sexual things to them. They might have you watch movies, or look at -pictures about sex.

Death: When someone you loves dies.

Top 10 IMPORTANT THINGS
ABOUT BAD THINGS THAT HAPPENED TO ME

_____

_____

_____

_____

_____

_____

_____

_____

_____

Bad Things that Happened to Me

What things have happened to me that I did not want to happen?

_____

_____

How did those things play a part in getting into trouble versus staying out of trouble?

_____

_____

What have been the biggest influences on how I made it through those experiences?

_____

_____

How did I keep myself going after bad things happened to me?

_____

_____

What am I learning about those bad things now?

_____

_____

What does it say about my courage, strength and respect?

_____

_____

What does this prove about me as a person?

_____

_____

How can I use what I know about the bad things that happened to make a successful change in my life?

_____

_____

How can the way I think about bad things that happened help me to become the person I want to be?

_____

_____

Violence and Abuse

While you're growing up you get a lot of messages about aggressive behavior. You get them from your parents, your brothers and sisters, aunts, uncles and grandparents. You also learn about these things from your friends and people outside of your family. Events that happen in your neighborhood and at school teach you about violence. You also learn a lot about violence and sexual aggression from television, video games, movies and books.

Thinking about violence and abuse can help you to figure out what messages you have received about them. It can also help you to consider how your personal experiences with violence and abuse have influenced getting into trouble versus staying out of trouble.

Some of the things you learn about violence and abuse are accurate and some of the things you learn might be wrong. Sometimes it's hard to know the difference. You might not know where to go to get the right answers. It's important to find answers that help you to tame violence and sexual aggression so you can take good care of yourself and stay out of trouble.

Taking time to identify things you have learned about violence can help you make sense of those messages. You can talk with others about how truthful the messages are. It can also help you to consider changing your thoughts about violence and abuse so that they no longer get you into trouble.

Violence

How have I experienced violence in my life?

_____

How has violence played a part in getting into trouble versus staying
out of trouble?

_____

What have been the biggest influences on how I made it through those
experiences?

_____

How did I keep myself going after being involved in violence?

_____

What does it say about my courage, strength and respect?

_____

What does this prove about me as a person?

_____

How can I use what I know about violence to make a successful
change in my life?

_____

Top 10
IMPORTANT THINGS ABOUT VIOLENCE

_____

_____

_____

_____

_____

_____

_____

_____

Abuse

Some bad things that happen to children are called "abuse". Abuse means hurting someone by treating him or her badly. The different kinds of abuse were listed with the bad things that happen in life. Someone saying hurtful things, over and over again, to you, or others, that cause you to feel badly about yourself, is called verbal abuse. Physical abuse happens when someone hurts your body and leaves marks of any kind. Sexual abuse occurs whenever someone uses you for his or her own sexual needs.

Emotional abuse is when someone makes you feel badly in a way that keeps you from being able to do things that you should be able to do as you are growing up. An example of this occurs when a parent, or older person, depends on a child to take care of them and prevents the child from doing things like playing with other children, or going to school. This can happen when an adult struggles with alcohol or drug addiction. It can also happen when children are ignored and neglected. When a child does not have an adult who takes good care of them the child doesn't learn how to get his, or her, needs met.

Sometimes children are abused by people they love the most. When this happens children often feel scared, alone and lonely. It becomes hard to trust others to take care of you. You might feel that it isn't safe to be in close relationships and you might have trouble connecting with others in helpful ways. You may tell yourself that it's better to be alone. These are normal reactions for children who have been abused by parents, other family members, or adults who were supposed to be taking good care of you.

Abuse

How have I experienced abuse in my life?

_____

How has abuse played a part in getting into trouble versus staying out of trouble?

_____

What have been the biggest influences on how I made it through abusive experiences?

_____

How did I keep myself going after being involved in abuse?

_____

What does it say about my courage, strength and respect?

_____

What does this prove about me as a person?

_____

How can I use what I know about abuse to make a successful change in my life?

_____

Top10 IMPORTANT THINGS ABOUT ABUSE

_____

_____

_____

_____

_____

_____

_____

Trauma

A trauma can be an injury, or a painful emotional experience, that has a lasting effect on your life. When others hurt you by saying bad things, hitting you, or touching you in sexual ways, it can hurt for a long time. The pain can be in your body, your mind, and in your heart. The pain that those things cause in your heart and mind often lasts longer than the pain they cause your body. Sometimes these bad things are called "trauma". A trauma is an injury, wound, or shock that causes a painful experience. Being away from people you care about is painful and can be traumatic. Even though a lot of people go through divorce it causes a great deal of pain. Losing a family member through separation or death can be quite traumatic.

There is a difference between bad things that happen and trauma. A lot of bad things that happen may only bother you for a short time. Some bad things may be awful when they happen, and for a while afterwards, but the pain goes away over time. You may even forget about them after a while. Pain from trauma can stick with you a long time, sometimes even your whole life. Even though a lot of the pain may go away, trauma is something you never forget.

All human beings need others to survive. It can be confusing when you're afraid to be close to others and still have a desire to be close to someone who treats you nicely. It's hard to believe that they won't turn against you. The trauma of past abuse can get in the way of having good relationships in your life right now. You can learn to understand abuse by talking with adults, who do not hurt you, about the information, and activities, in this book. This can help you to learn how to take good care of yourself.

Trauma

What bad things that happened to me were traumatic?

_____

How have those traumas played a part in getting into trouble versus staying out of trouble?

_____

What have been the biggest influences on how I made it through those traumatic experiences?

_____

How did I keep myself going after those traumas?

_____

What does this say about my courage, strength and respect?

_____

What does this prove about me as a person?

_____

How can I use what I know about trauma to make a successful change in my life?

_____

Top10 IMPORTANT THINGS ABOUT TRAUMA

_____

_____

_____

_____

_____

_____

_____

Conclusion

Whew! You have just completed a lot more hard work. Good for you! You have been getting a lot of practice being thoughtful about your life. This practice can create new ways for you to think about managing challenging experiences. This might be a good time to think back, or reflect, on what you have learned from this section.

REFLECTIONS ON BAD THINGS THAT HAPPEN IN LIFE

How hard was it to answer all of the questions about bad things that happen in life?

_____

_____

What did it take to face up and write about those bad things?

_____

_____

What have I proved about my courage, strength and respect in facing them?

_____

_____

What have I proved about myself as a person?

_____

_____

What challenges am I facing about the bad things that happened to me?

_____

_____

How can I use this new information to tame violence and sexual aggression?

_____

_____

What will help me prepare to go on to the next section of the workbook?

_____

_____

chapter four: Feeding Violence and Sexual Aggression

Power and control and connection are basic needs that influence a lot of human behavior. Everyone wants something in life and everyone has a desire to manage, or direct, how things happen. All human beings must connect with others in order to stay alive. These things are all related to feeling good about yourself. The more you learn about them and understand how they influence behavior the more success you can have in taming violence and sexual aggression.

For many years people have been saying that violence and sexual assault are about power and control. You may have been told this and you may be focusing some of your treatment on these issues. Abusive use of power and control play a part in decisions to commit acts of violence and sexual aggression. They are not the only things that influence decisions to hurt people in such ways.

The ways you learn to connect with others plays a big part in getting into trouble versus staying out of trouble. When children are treated respectfully with care and concern they learn to treat others the same way. When children do not receive love in a way that helps them to grow and do well, connection with others can be confusing and scary. Such confusion and fear may influence a child to behave in harmful ways.

Secrecy provides a way to hide criminal acts and also plays a part in violence and sexual aggression. When pain from experiencing bad things feels unmanageable some people get confused and try to cover up the pain with anger. Desperate and confused needs for power and control and connection, mixed up with secrecy, can influence misdirected anger that results in violence and sexual aggression.

This section of the workbook addresses how abusive use of power, control and connection feed on secrecy and anger to influence violence and sexual aggression. It also addresses ways that you can consider using power and control in helpful ways. When you are able to do this, connection with others is based upon care, concern and compassion. Letting go of destructive secrets enables people to honestly address needs for power, control and connection in ways that no longer cause harm. This work is a big step in taming violence and sexual aggression.

Connection

Connection is like attachment, which means to connect by ties of affection or devotion. Connection is about how people relate to others. It particularly relates to close family ties and how people act towards those closest to them. Connection means joining together with, and relation between things. Connection can also mean an influential person through whom one can get special favors.

How parents behave towards children impacts how children relate to others. When children receive love and affection, and are well cared for, it is easy to feel close to others and to trust that good things can happen in life. When children do not receive this type of care it can be difficult to learn how to connect with others. All human beings need connection through human touch in order to stay alive. When people are in need of human connection, or attachment, they reach out to touch and to be touched. When they connect with others through affection they can trust that their needs will be met. This might be a handshake, or a pat on the back. If it is someone they are close to it might be a hug and/or a kiss.

When children have not had supportive attachments they cannot trust that touch will be affectionate. When children have been abused they might assume that connection is hurtful. They may be afraid to connect with others. However, since everyone needs to be touched, they may try to connect with others in harmful ways. If a child feels desperate to be touched he, or she, may lash out in violent, or sexually aggressive ways, just to feel connection with someone else. If they have been touched in hurtful ways, they might think that it is okay to touch others in hurtful ways. This type of connection is dangerous and causes a lot of problems.

Even though you may have had experiences similar to this, you can learn to connect with others in wonderful ways. You have opportunities every day to develop attachments that are based upon care and concern and affection. You can learn to touch others in ways that make them feel good and that can make you feel great! It sometimes takes practice but it's worth it.

Connection

How do the ways I experience connection in my life play a part in getting into trouble versus staying out of trouble?

_____

_____

What have been the biggest influences on how I experience connection with others?

_____

_____

What am I learning about connection now?

_____

_____

What challenges am I facing about the ways I connect with others?

_____

_____

How is this new information helping me to find courage, strength and respect?

_____

_____

How can I use what I know about connection to make a successful change in my life?

_____

_____

Top 10 IMPORTANT
THINGS ABOUT CONNECTING WITH OTHERS

_____

_____

_____

_____

_____

_____

_____

_____

Top 10 BENEFITS OF
TOUCH AND CONNECTION

1. Receiving care

2. Soothing

3. Companionship

4. Enjoyment

5. Giving love

6. Relaxation

7. Feeling calm

8. Feeling close

9. Healing

10. Receiving love

Power

Power is something that has a lot of meanings. It is an ability to do something, or a capacity to exert force or energy. It is when a person has great influence or authority to rule, govern or dominate. Power can also describe strength and vigor. Vigor is active physical or mental force. Power is not good or bad. It's just power. All human beings have a desire for power. Everyone strives to develop an ability to do something, no matter how simple it may be. Most everyone develops a lot of abilities that are related to power. You have power to keep shoes on your feet by mastering the skill it takes to tie shoelaces so they don't fall off. Everyone has power to attract attention through the use of words and actions. A desire to influence others energizes people to be helpful. Obtaining knowledge to increase mental force, or brain power, does a lot of good. Power can influence how we think about ourselves and how others think about us.

There is a wide range of how power is used in this world. How power is used influences its value. A lot of people use power to do good things and to make our world a better place to live. Some people have personal power that comes from being strong, courageous, smart, kind and good. Other people have power that comes from a position they are in such as an elected official, a corporate officer, a teacher or minister. Some people have both personal and positional power. *When power is used to make things better and to benefit people it is called benevolence, or benevolent power.* Most truly powerful people obtain that power from using their education to obtain things that are important to them.

Brian was three years old when his father was arrested and sent to prison and his grandfather killed himself. Even though he was little he thought of himself as king of the house since his father and grandfather were gone and he was the oldest child. His parents got divorced and Brian was sexually abused by older boys over the next several years. He began having problems in school and started stealing. He was beaten for those things but kept having the same problems and more. Since he thought he was king of the house he believed that he could do whatever he wanted.

After he was arrested Brian learned a lot of things about power and control, secrecy and anger. Brian realized that his life felt out of control and that he thought he was powerless to make anything better. Instead of talking with someone about those feelings he acted on them in dangerous and abusive ways. He decided that being king of the house was getting him into trouble and that he might be able to stay out of trouble by giving up the throne and thinking of himself as a prince who could benefit by the support and encouragement of caring adults.

The president of the United States is often considered the most powerful man in the world. His power is both personal and positional. His personal power comes from having a personality that people like and want to vote for. His personal power also comes from his beliefs about what he thinks is best for the country. This is why people vote for him. His positional power comes from all of the resources that helped him to get elected and into his position as president. These things are education and money and personal connections with other powerful people. Once he's elected, a president uses his power in a lot of different ways. We all hope that a president will use his power to help make our lives better.

There are also times when people use power to hurt others. This is called abusive power. This is the kind of quest for power that influences violence and sexual aggression. It might come from confusion about painful experiences that a person felt powerless to manage. It might occur because someone was taught to hurt others through the use of violence or sexual aggression. It might also come from a desire to be mean to others. Wherever it comes from, it is a way that people use force and domination to cause pain.

Making sense of things you have learned about power can help you to understand how you have come to use it in abusive ways. It can also help you to consider using power in good ways. Many people believe that benevolence is the highest form of power. If you really want to be powerful consider all of the ways you can use the force of your energy to gain influence. You can use your personal power to learn to take good care of yourself. You can use it to do good things. Using power in this way will influence others to look up to you as an honorable and courageous young man! Good things come to people who use power benevolently.

Top 10
IMPORTANT THINGS ABOUT POWER

_____

_____

_____

_____

_____

_____

_____

_____

_____

Top 10 WAYS I
CAN PRACTICE USING BENEVOLENT POWER

_____

_____

_____

_____

_____

_____

_____

Power

How does power play a part in getting into trouble versus staying out of trouble?

_____

What have been the biggest influences on how I use power?

_____

What do I think about power now?

_____

Who comes to mind when I think of a person who uses power benevolently?

_____

What challenges am I facing about power?

_____

What does it say about my courage, strength and respect?

_____

How can I use what I know about power to make a successful change in my life?

_____

Control

Control means to exercise authority over, to direct, or command. Just like power, control is not good or bad. It's just control. Everybody wants to have some control in life. Control can be as basic as adjusting a thermostat so that the air in a room is warmer or cooler. Control gets more complicated when it comes to learning how to drive a car or controlling behavior. It can be very confusing when it feels like things are out of control and you don't know how to get control. Learning to control your thoughts, feelings and actions can help you to feel powerful. It can help you to make decisions about getting into trouble versus staying out of trouble and it can help you take good care of yourself.

Acts of violence and sexual abuse are out-of-control behaviors. They occur when people think that they have no other way to manage, or control, a difficult situation. You actually have a lot of other ways to experience control. You can gain greater control of your life by educating yourself about things that are important to you. The knowledge you are gaining here can help you out when you are feeling that life is out of control. It can help you to figure out what you would like to have greater control of so that you can tame violence and sexual aggression. It can keep you from spending your life in prison. Taking control of your life is about having freedom to become the person you want to be and to pursue your dreams.

Control

How does control play a part in getting into trouble versus staying out of trouble?

_____

_____

What have been the biggest influences on how I experience control in my life?

_____

_____

What am I learning about my needs for control?

_____

_____

What challenges am I facing about control?

_____

_____

How is this learning helping me to find courage, strength and respect?

_____

_____

How can I use what I know about control to make a successful change in my life?

_____

_____

Top 10 IMPORTANT THINGS ABOUT CONTROL

_____

_____

_____

_____

_____

_____

_____

_____

_____

_____

Secrecy

When it comes to violence and sexual aggression, secrets are poison! Keeping information about violence and abuse secret is very dangerous and can influence criminal behavior. Secrecy means to hide something. Violence and sexual aggression depend a lot on secrecy in order to maintain the threat of abusive power and control. When someone has the courage and strength to report crimes they are no longer secret and can be brought to the attention of people who can help stop them.

Secrets confuse the difference between telling and "tattling". Telling is reporting information to get help. Tattling is telling on someone in order to get him or her in trouble. It can be easier to break the spell of secrecy when you know that telling the truth can help someone, often yourself.

There are differences between secrecy and privacy and confidentiality. While privacy and confidentiality address the personal nature of information and relationships, secrecy is about hiding these things. The benefits of solitude, privacy and confidential relationships will be addressed in chapter six which is about taking good care of yourself.

Secrecy

How does secrecy play a part in getting into trouble versus staying out of trouble?

_____

_____

What have been the biggest influences on how I experience secrecy?

_____

_____

What am I learning about secrecy now?

_____

_____

What challenges am I facing about keeping secrets?

_____

_____

How is this new information helping me to find courage, strength and respect?

_____

_____

How can I use what I know about secrecy to make a successful change in my life?

_____

_____

Top 10 IMPORTANT
THINGS ABOUT GETTING RID OF SECRETS

_____

_____

_____

_____

_____

_____

_____

_____

Anger

Anger is a feeling of distress. It results from injury and mistreatment and often shows itself in a desire to fight back at the supposed cause of this feeling. When bad things happen, feelings of fear and power-lessness are often present. You may feel like things are out of control. When you feel powerless, and out of control, you may want to get away from such feelings. This is where anger comes into the picture.

Anger can be an important motivation to right a wrong. But anger can fool you when it influences you to lash out against injustice. When it causes harm, it brings more pain and does not solve the problem, or take away the pain. When this happens, anger adds to the problem, and makes things worse.

Young people who commit acts of violence and sexual aggression are struggling with anger that they haven't found a way to control. It might be that you have not been able to find a way to forgive people who have hurt you. Your desire to lash out at others may be your way of trying to punish others who caused you pain and trauma. When you don't know how to manage pain you might try to disguise it as anger. But it's still pain. Anger can be a desperate attempt to cover up pain that feels unmanageable.

Attending to pain prevents it from being turned into anger. Learning to face pain means that you can heal rather than stay angry. Resentment doesn't build up when you work to heal pain in your life at the time that it occurs.

Top 10 WAYS
I CAN EXPRESS ANGER RESPECTFULLY

_____

_____

_____

_____

_____

_____

_____

Anger

How does anger play a part in getting into trouble versus staying out of trouble?

_____

_____

What have been the biggest influences on how I deal with anger?

_____

_____

What am I learning about anger now?

_____

_____

What challenges am I facing about the ways I manage anger?

_____

_____

How is this new information helping me to find courage, strength and respect?

_____

_____

How can I use what I know about anger to make a successful change in my life?

_____

_____

Conclusion

You have just spent a lot of time exploring some of the big ticket items that influence decisions to commit acts of violence and sexual aggression. Way to go! Many people take a lot longer to figure these things out, and some people never do. By making sense of how you want to experience power, control, and connection in your life you are able to really consider how you want to take good care of yourself. When you make the decision to give up secrecy you are daring to take a stand for yourself and begin taming violence and sexual aggression. When you have the courage to accept pain without attempting to turn it into anger you become stronger and able to bear pain without allowing it to cause problems in your life.

Human connection is a very powerful motivation in life. A quest for power and control can fool people into thinking that those things are most important, but that's not true. Many boys are lead to believe that intimacy and close loving connections to significant others are not important, or are a sign of weakness. This is not true either! Genuine strength comes from a sense of security about yourself. Learning that you have value and are worthwhile comes from supportive and loving relations with others. When you know this about yourself you are able to consider what kind of caring relationships you want to have with yourself and anyone you choose to be close to.

REFLECTIONS ON FEEDING VIOLENCE AND SEXUAL AGGRESSION

How has it been helpful to answer questions about things that feed violence and sexual aggression?

_____

_____

What am I continuing to prove about my courage, strength and respect in facing them?

_____

_____

How is it helping me to think about myself differently?

_____

_____

What does this prove about me as a person?

_____

_____

How can I use this new information to tame violence and sexual aggression?

_____

_____

How can the way I think about things that feed violence and sexual aggression help me to become the person I want to be?

_____

_____

What will help me prepare to go on to the next section of the workbook?

_____

_____

Top 10 BENEFITS OF HEALING

1. Feeling less pain

2. Seeking truth

3. Enjoying life

4. Learning about benevolence

5. Exploring well being

6. Practicing honor

7. Feeling good about yourself

8. Accepting love

9. Considering intimacy

10. Forgiveness

Healing

Learning how to handle difficult things, such as trauma, without causing harm is a way you can heal pain in your life and stay out of trouble. *To "heal" means to make well, as in the word "healthy".* Healing can help you tame violence and sexual aggression. You can learn how to protect yourself and you can learn how protecting yourself can help you stop hurting others. When you practice doing things differently you might be surprised at how much better you feel. You might be surprised to learn that you can feel powerful without hurting others. You might also be surprised to learn that you can control most of the trouble in your life. You can be close to others and learn to touch, and be touched, in ways that can make you feel great!

This section of the workbook focuses on ways you can heal pain so that you can become the person you want to be and pursue your dreams. Remember that benevolence is a desire to do good. It is kind and charitable action. Healing occurs through benevolence. Benevolence can be directed towards yourself and others. When you are able to accept the kindness and care of people who genuinely want to help you tame violence and sexual aggression you are taking a stand for healing. Like respect, benevolence is both given and received. It takes practice to be good at giving and receiving.

J.R. experienced a lot of confusing things in his life. He was taken away from his mother when he was an infant because she drank alcohol a lot and neglected him. He had not seen his father since he was five years old and he did not know why. In a meeting with a counselor he was told that he had been sexually abused while visiting his father, but he didn't remember that.

When he went to school he didn't know what his last name was. J.R. thought it was different than what the teacher said it was. J.R. remembered being beaten with switches by his father's ex-wife and he recalled trying to burn up one of his mother's boyfriends who treated him badly. J.R. thought his mother loved her other children more than him. He was hurt and confused by those things and he got in trouble by sexually abusing his sister and by breaking into his father's home and stealing.

chapter five: The Trauma Outcome Process

The trauma outcome process is a tool that helps people to heal from painful life experiences. It can be confusing so plan to talk with people you trust about how it can be helpful. Pace yourself, and take it easy. Working through this information slowly is an important step for healing. It is a way that you are practicing benevolence, as you are being kind to yourself when you allow yourself time to think things through.

Confusion

There are a lot of reasons why you decided to commit acts of violence or sexual aggression. It's easy to get confused about all of the things that go on in life. When you have pain in your heart from bad things that happened to you it's very confusing. Sometimes confusion influences people to cause harm. The bad things you did are the result, or outcome, of decisions and choices you made in response to pain.

Steps you can take to ease confusion are called a process. This is why the workbook is called T.O.P.*. T.O.P.* stands for Trauma Outcome Process. These are steps you can take to stop hurting yourself, and others, by figuring out new ways to manage pain caused by past trauma in you life.

_____

_____

_____

_____

_____

_____

_____

_____

_____

_____

the trauma outcome process

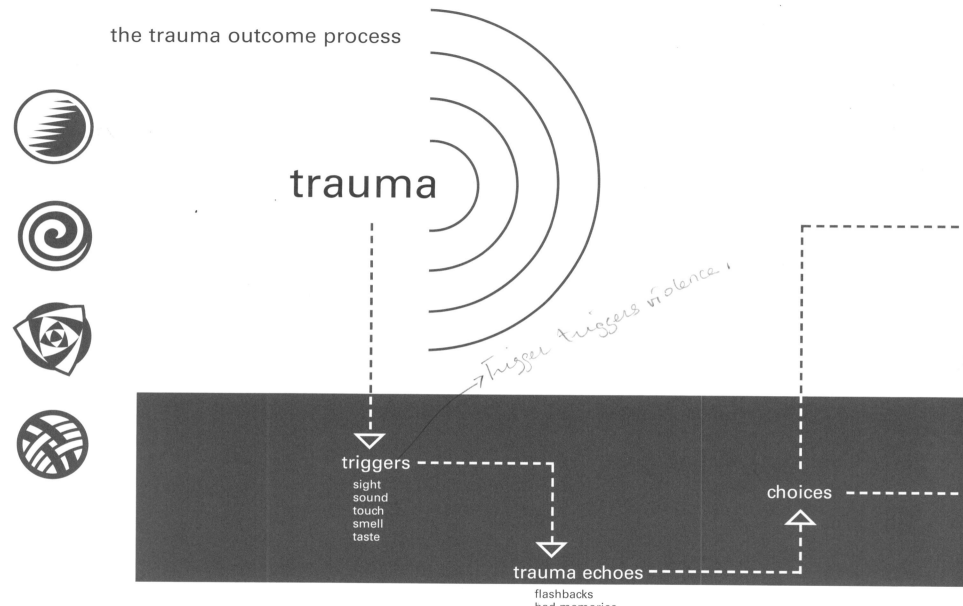

trauma

Trigger triggers violence!

triggers
sight
sound
touch
smell
taste

trauma echoes
flashbacks
bad memories
nightmares
night terrors

choices

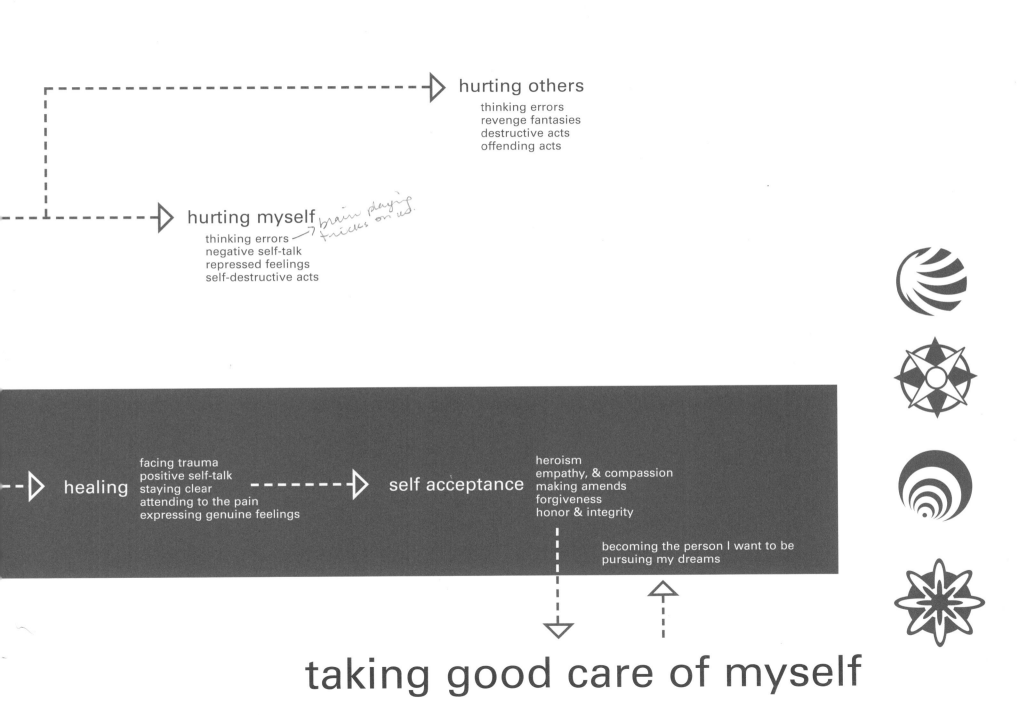

hurting others

thinking errors
revenge fantasies
destructive acts
offending acts

hurting myself *→ brain playing tricks on us.*

thinking errors
negative self-talk
repressed feelings
self-destructive acts

healing

facing trauma
positive self-talk
staying clear
attending to the pain
expressing genuine feelings

self acceptance

heroism
empathy, & compassion
making amends
forgiveness
honor & integrity

becoming the person I want to be
pursuing my dreams

taking good care of myself

Trauma

Recognizing bad things that happened in your life is a step towards healing pain that those things cause. When you are able to recognize them, it may hurt, but at least you are clear about what's causing the pain. Once you know where pain is coming from you can figure out what you need to do to stop it. Instead of feeling like the pain makes you lose control, you can learn to control it. When you learn to control pain, in ways that do not cause harm, you begin to heal.

Taking good care of yourself requires identifying bad things that have happened to you. You began doing this in the last section and will focus more on it now. Please take some more time to think about those things and add any new things you remember so that you can be successful in making sense of them. It can still be scary to do this so you might want to have someone you trust help you with it. They can help you to feel safe while you find the courage and strength to face up to the painful events. Sometimes pain caused by trauma comes up in unexpected ways and catches you by surprise. These situations can be scary, confusing and really hard to manage. It might be hard but you can learn to figure them out so that it's not so painful.

Triggers

For ten years Calvin reacted to triggers that brought up the old pain and he got into serious trouble. He was arrested and sent away for two years.

Calvin decided to tell his mom about some bad things that happened to him when he was little that she didn't know about. After he told her he felt very anxious and nervous. That evening he tried to pick a fight with another boy. The next morning he was still upset and started crying at breakfast. He didn't want anyone to see him crying so he got up and ran out. He ran into two staff and began hitting them. They held him down for twenty minutes before he was able to go to a safe place.

Calvin figured out that talking about the bad things triggered him back to a time when he had been abused. He felt help-less, powerless and out of control. When he was little he didn't think it was safe enough to tell his mom about it.

Most people have five senses. They are sight, sound, touch, smell, and taste. These senses tell your brain what's going on around you. People generally manage pain from trauma pretty well and don't think about it all of the time. Then, all of a sudden, painful feelings come up that remind you of bad things that happened in your life. These are called "triggers". *A trigger is something that sets off an action*. A trigger event is a specific thing that reminds you of a past trauma in your life. An example of this is when you see someone who reminds you of somebody who hurt you in the past. Your sense of sight is triggering your brain to remember the pain that the first person caused you. It then influences you to act in response to the bad feelings that it brings up. In the past triggers like that may have caused you to act in ways that hurt yourself and others. It doesn't have to be that way.

Once you begin to practice identifying triggers you can learn to think more about them and slow down your reactions. *A reaction is a return, or opposing action or force*. It is an action brought on by resistance to another action. When people react to a trigger they are at risk of acting in ways that will get them into trouble. You can learn to identify it, think about it, and consider a wise response. *A response is a positive or favorable answer*. You can learn to respond to triggers in ways that do not cause harm to yourself or others. You can learn to respond rather than react.

Here's an activity to help you start making sense of your own trauma outcome process.

Things That Trigger Thoughts and Feelings About My Own Trauma

Things I see:

_____

Things I smell:

_____

Things I taste:

_____

Things I touch:

_____

Things I hear:

_____

Others Who Touch Me:

_____

Triggers

When am I successful in managing triggers without causing any harm?

_____

_____

What does this prove about myself and how I practice courage, strength and respect?

_____

_____

How can I use this new information to tame violence and sexual aggression?

_____

_____

How can I use what I know about triggers to make a successful change in my life?

_____

_____

Top 10 IMPORTANT THINGS
ABOUT RECOGNIZING TRIGGER EVENTS

_____

_____

_____

_____

_____

_____

_____

_____

Trauma Echoes

When you get triggered to remember bad things that happened to you it can seem like the trauma is happening all over again, right now. It's like an echo. *An echo is something that imitates something else and keeps coming back, or repeating itself.* When bad things that happened in the past are triggered in your mind it's called a "trauma echo".

Trauma echoes effect your feelings, thoughts and actions. When an echo is triggered your body can respond very fast. You may become tense and feel your body tighten up. You may clench your fists, or feel your blood heat up your neck and face. You may catch your breath or have trouble breathing. You might feel like you want to run away as fast as you can, or you may feel like you want to fight. When your body does these things your thoughts can be racing really fast in you head. You may feel confused and struggle to figure out what's going on in your brain. You might feel powerless to do anything about it. You may think and feel like the bad thing is actually happening again. This is called a "flashback". Trauma echoes can also be bad memories, bad dreams, nightmares or night terrors. When you experience trauma echoes you might think that you are out of control, but you're not.

Calvin realized he was reacting to trauma echoes when he was picking fights that got him into trouble. He told a counselor that he didn't like violence and he dared to take a stand to stop the violence in his life. He decided to start talking to staff about things that were bothering him instead of fighting. He got the courage to tell his family and they supported his struggle to stay out of trouble.

Trauma Echoes

How do trauma echoes play a part in getting into trouble versus staying out of trouble?

_____

I've had flashbacks to....

_____

I've had bad dreams, or nightmares, about....

_____

Painful memories include...

_____

When do I successfully manage trauma echoes without causing any harm?

_____

What does this prove about me and how I practice courage, strength and respect?

_____

How can I use this new information to tame violence and sexual aggression?

_____

Top 10 IMPORTANT
THINGS ABOUT TRAUMA ECHOES

_____

_____

_____

_____

_____

_____

_____

_____

Choices

The good news is that you have choices. Yes, choices! Even when things are happening so fast you can make choices about how you act. When you were getting into trouble you may not have realized that you had choices about how you could respond to trauma echoes. If you felt powerless, and out of control, you may have tried to gain control of the situation by using abusive power in criminal ways. Finding the courage and strength to make choices that don't cause more pain, is the most important part of learning to heal pain and take good care of yourself. I'll bet there have been times when you were struggling in this way and you made choices to stay out of trouble. Think about those times. The times you have been successful will help you to be even more successful! It's like those home runs that were mentioned earlier in the workbook.

In the past, when you hurt yourself, or others, you made choices to do so. Your mind was thinking in a way that was telling you to do bad things. You have the power to make it think differently. You can control your actions and stop causing more pain.

Choices

How have trauma echoes played a part in getting into trouble versus staying out of trouble?

_____

How have I hurt others?

_____

How have I hurt myself?

_____

When have I responded to a trauma echo and chosen to stay out of trouble?

_____

What does this prove about my choices to be courageous, strong and respectful?

_____

How am I choosing to heal from my own trauma?

_____

How can I use what I know about choices to make a successful change in my life?

_____

Top 10 IMPORTANT
THINGS ABOUT MAKING CHOICES

_____

_____

_____

_____

_____

_____

_____

_____

Thinking Errors About Hurting Others

Some messages that you have received about violence and sexual aggression have influenced you to think in ways that are not correct. These are called "thinking errors". Trauma can cause people to create, and believe, thinking errors. If you were abused in the past you may think that everyone abuses children. This is a thinking error. Most people go through life and never abuse others. If you were mistreated by adults you may think that all adults hurt children. This is a thinking error. Most adults treat children with love and care. If someone you loved got sick and died, you may think that anyone you love will leave you. This is a thinking error. Most people have loving relationships throughout their lives. If you don't get to see your dad, you may think that all dads don't care about their children. This is a thinking error. Most father's care deeply about their children. If bad things happened to a lot of people you know, it makes sense that you might have thinking errors. But they're still not accurate.

Thinking Errors and Revenge Fantasies

How do thinking errors and revenge fantasies play a part in getting into trouble versus staying out of trouble?

_____

_____

What thinking errors and revenge fantasies have caused me problems in the past?

_____

_____

What makes me want to get revenge?

_____

_____

When am I successful in taming thinking errors and revenge fantasies?

_____

_____

How is this new information helping me to take a stand for courage, strength and respect?

_____

_____

How can I use what I know about thinking errors and revenge fantasies to make a successful change in my life?

_____

_____

Revenge Fantasies

When you have a trauma echo, thinking errors can get in the way of making good choices. This is a problem. When you believe a thinking error, it has the power to cause you problems. If you believe that everyone hurts others and you get triggered back to a bad thing that happened to you, you might think something like "I better get them before they get me". This kind of thinking can only get you in more trouble. When you create fantasies to hurt others you're in danger of causing more pain.

Fantasies are unfulfilled desires. These are thoughts about doing something you think you might like to do but normally would not do. Revenge fantasies are a desire to get back at someone and hurt them. This type of fantasy can lead you into doing things that destroy relationships and get you arrested. If you think that getting revenge can heal your pain, you're wrong! Revenge fantasies can fool you into thinking that hurting others is okay. When they're over, you may feel worse about yourself.

Take some time to think about how your thoughts effect your actions. How does your thinking influence the way you manage upsetting experiences caused by trauma echoes. The more you know about your thinking errors and revenge fantasies the more you will be able to expect and prepare for them. This will allow you to make a plan for practicing making choices that do not cause anyone harm others.

Top 10 IMPORTANT THINGS ABOUT TAMING THINKING ERRORS AND REVENGE FANTASIES

_____

_____

_____

_____

_____

_____

_____

_____

Top 10 THINKING ERRORS ABOUT REVENGE FANTASIES

1. Everybody's out to get me

2. All people are bad

3. Nothing I do matters

4. I can't trust anybody

5. Nobody can hurt me

6. Nobody cares about me

7. I can have sex whenever I want it

8. Anyone who loves me will hurt me

9. Everybody cheats

10. I can do anything I want

Destructive Acts

A destructive act is anything someone does that hurts someone or something. Destructive acts include things like saying bad things to, or about, someone. Being rude and disrespectful are destructive acts. Destructive acts also include destroying things. These are things that can hurt your relationships but don't get you in trouble with the law. Destructive acts get you in trouble with other people. They are dishonorable and get in the way of respectful connection with others.

Offending Acts

Offending acts are criminal acts that get you in trouble with the law. Laws tell you what specific offenses are and which ones people should be arrested for. Your violent or sexual offenses are what got you in trouble and brought you into treatment. People who chose to hurt others through their trauma outcome process often commit both destructive and offending acts.

Carlos used to say hateful things and call his mother awful names. He seldom did what he was asked and ended up dropping out of school. He never got arrested for those things but they prevented him from having respectful relationships with others.

Top 10 IMPORTANT THINGS ABOUT STOPPING DESTRUCTIVE AND OFFENDING BEHAVIOR

_____

_____

_____

_____

_____

_____

_____

_____

_____

Destructive and Offending Acts

What have been the biggest influences on how I experience destructive and offending acts?

_____

_____

When was I likely to behave destructively or commit a criminal offense?

_____

_____

What destructive things have I done to cause harm?

_____

_____

What offenses have I committed that were against the law?

_____

_____

Who has been hurt by my destructive and criminal behavior?

_____

_____

What damage did my criminal acts cause?

_____

_____

When am I successful in taming the urge to commit destructive and offensive acts?

_____

_____

What does this new information prove about my courage, strength and respect?

_____

_____

How does it show that I can use power, control and connection in helpful ways?

_____

_____

What does it say about my efforts to tame violence and sexual aggression?

_____

_____

How can I use what I know about destructive and offending acts to make a successful change in my life?

_____

_____

1. I'm bad

2. It's all my fault

3. I'm stupid

4. I can't do anything right

5. Nobody could ever like me

6. I'm untrustworthy

7. I'm worthless

8. I don't feel anything

9. Nobody cares

10. Nothing is ever going to change

Thinking Errors About Hurting Myself

Another type of thinking error is believing that bad things that happened to you were your fault, when they were not. Bad things can happen through no fault of your own. Some bad things that happen may be your fault. Sometimes bad things just happen and it's nobody's fault. If you were abused in any way it was not your fault. No matter how badly you might behave no one has the right to abuse you. Abuse is against the law. If you think that you are to blame for things that were not your fault this is a shame.

People create thinking errors when they do not have clear information about things that happen. If people who hurt you said things like "you're no good" or "it's all your fault", you might believe them. Those things are not true! You may have done bad things but that doesn't mean that you are bad. It just means you've done some bad things.

Many children whose parents get divorced blame themselves for the breakup of their parent's marriage. This is a thinking error. Adults get divorced because they do not want to be together any more. Divorce seldom has anything to do with children. Take some time to pay attention to any thinking errors that you may be struggling with.

Negative Self-Talk

Thinking errors about causing bad things, or blaming yourself for things that were not your fault, can lead you to tell yourself bad things. Negative self-talk can influence hurting yourself. This can be very dangerous.

Calvin had a thinking error that "tears are bad". He went to great lengths to avoid tears. He began telling himself that "when I cry I want to hit something". He would often hit walls with his hands or bang his head against a wall to try to manage pain without crying. It didn't work, and Calvin didn't realize until he was in treatment that hurting his hands and head were just adding problems instead of solving them. Calvin learned to accept tears as a normal response to pain. He realized that there are times when he needs to cry about the pain there is in his life. He prefers to do so privately but he knows that tears are an important part of healing.

Thinking Errors and Negative Self-Talk

How do thinking errors and negative self-talk play a part in getting into trouble versus staying out of trouble?

_____

_____

What thinking errors and negative self-talk have caused me problems?

_____

_____

What makes me want to hurt myself?

_____

_____

When am I successful in taming thinking errors and negative self-talk that play a part in hurting myself?

_____

_____

What does this prove about my courage, strength and respect for myself?

_____

_____

How is this new information helping me to use power, control and connection in helpful ways?

_____

_____

How can I use what I know about thinking errors and negative self-talk to make a successful change in my life?

_____

_____

Top 10 IMPORTANT THINGS
ABOUT TAMING NEGATIVE SELF-TALK

_____

_____

_____

_____

_____

_____

_____

_____

Repressed Feelings

To repress means to keep down or hold back. Repression also means to control so strictly as to prevent natural expression. Repressed feelings are those emotions that you try to run away from, or bury them somewhere inside of you. When you keep talking to yourself in negative ways you may try to push the bad thoughts and feelings away so you don't have to think about them, or feel them. That takes a lot of energy! It's like you're running away from yourself. Every time you have a trauma echo and you try to run away from it, or push it aside, things get worse. The bad thoughts just keep filling up inside of you and you're trying so hard to run away from them, or push them away, that you get worn out. When this happens you don't have energy to talk to people, you don't have energy to feel anything, and you don't have energy to heal the pain. These things can influence you to hurt yourself.

After a while you may feel numb. *Numb is feeling weakened, or deprived of the power of feeling or moving.* It is almost impossible to take good care of yourself when you are numb. Experiencing numbness prevents you from being aware of what is happening to you and how things are impacting you.

Taking time to think about how you have tried to repress feelings about certain things can help you to figure out how life experiences can influence you to cause pain. When you know what you have been trying to push aside, or run away from, you can stand tall and face it head on. You can use your strength and courage to tackle pain. You can dare to take a stand for yourself.

Be careful as you are answering these questions, as you might feel vulnerable for a while. You might feel confused and impatient. You might also feel scared so make sure you are safe. You might want to have someone you trust with you. When you are willing to face pain you may worry that you won't know what to do with it. You might begin to feel emotions that come with pain. Some of those feelings might be horror, loneliness and isolation. When you accept the feelings of pain and grief about bad things that have happened to you healing is occurring. The intensity of pain can be terrifying. Facing that pain is an important way that healing truly occurs. When you have courage to face the pain you realize that you are able to go through it and come out on the other side. This is healing. You can do it.

Repressed Feelings

How do repressed feelings play a part in getting into trouble versus staying out of trouble?

_____

What life experiences caused me to try to turn off, or repress feelings?

_____

What thoughts and feelings scare me?

_____

When do I successfully face pain?

_____

What does this prove about my courage and strength?

_____

How is this new information helping me to use power, control and connection in helpful ways?

_____

How can I use what I know about repressed feelings to make a successful change in my life?

_____

Top 10 IMPORTANT THINGS ABOUT FEELINGS

_____

_____

_____

_____

_____

_____

_____

_____

Self-Destructive Acts

When you don't know how, or don't have energy, to take good care of yourself trauma echoes can influence you to hurt yourself. Self-destructive acts are any behaviors that cause harm to yourself. People who haven't found the strength and courage to make sense of their trauma outcome process are often confused in their efforts to manage pain. Since thoughts and feelings get so mixed up it's not surprising that self-destructive acts can be part of that confusion. A lot of people who have hurt others have also hurt themselves in a variety of ways.

Some acts of self-destruction are easy to identify like smoking, drinking alcohol, or taking drugs and attempting suicide. Some self-destructive behavior is hard to figure out. It is self-destructive to hang out in dangerous places, drive recklessly, hit walls or pick fights. You can hurt yourself by eating too much or too little. Scratching or rubbing yourself until you bleed and cause sores are called self-mutilation. Mutilation means to damage or injure. Mutilation is very dangerous! You don't have to do those things. Self-harm is just another way of confusing painful thoughts and feelings. Self-destructive acts never heal pain. They create more pain. You can find ways to stop such confusion that don't involve hurting yourself.

Self-Destructive Acts

What have been the biggest influences on how I treat myself?

_____

_____

What harmful things have I done to myself?

_____

_____

When was I likely to do those things?

_____

_____

When am I successful in taming the urge to hurt myself?

_____

_____

What does this prove about courage, strength and respect for myself?

_____

_____

How does it prove that I can use power, control and connection in helpful ways?

_____

_____

How can I use what I know about self-destructive acts to make a successful change in my life?

_____

_____

Top 10 IMPORTANT THINGS
TO STOP SELF-DESTRUCTIVE BEHAVIOR

_____

_____

_____

_____

_____

_____

_____

_____

Conclusion

Once again it's time to give yourself credit for all of the hard work you have been doing. I hope that you are getting a lot of good feedback about your efforts. This is extremely important work and you deserve a lot of credit! I recommend that you take some time to let all of this information settle in.

In this section you have focused a great deal on making sense of how bad things that happened to you come back through a trauma outcome process. That process influenced you to make choices that have caused harm to yourself and others. Everyone faces this same challenge in life because everyone experiences trauma. It takes constant practice to manage your trauma outcome process in ways that do not cause harm. This is how you tame violence and sexual aggression.

REFLECTIONS ON THE TRAUMA OUTCOME PROCESS

How has it been helpful to answer questions about the trauma outcome process?

_____

_____

What has the trauma outcome process taught me about myself?

_____

_____

What did it take to face up to my trauma outcome process?

_____

_____

What am I proving about myself as a person?

_____

_____

What can I do with this information that will help me tame violence and sexual aggression?

_____

_____

Who would I like to share the trauma outcome process with in order to help them heal some of the pain in their life.

_____

_____

What will help me prepare to go on to the next section of the workbook?

_____

_____

chapter six: Taking Good Care of Yourself

You have already been practicing taking good care of yourself by answering the questions in this workbook. When it comes to taming violence and sexual aggression, the trauma outcome process gives you a way of better understanding your thoughts, feelings and actions relating to bad things that have happened in your life. This section can help you to create a plan for practicing successful ways of managing pain.

Facing Trauma

Recognizing trauma is a big task. You have been doing this since completing the section about bad things that happen in life. You may think of other things you forgot and can add them to your answers. There may be other things that have happened since you filled out those answers. There are always bad things that happen in life. The more open you are to face trauma, and attend to pain that it causes, the better able you are to take good care of yourself. Letting people you trust know that there is pain in your life is not a weakness. It is actually an act of courage and strength. Truly strong people are able to acknowledge pain without allowing it to cause more pain. To dare to stand tall and describe your experiences and declare that the bad things have not gotten the best of you is an act of power and control. It is proof that you can use the power of words and connection to tame the violence and sexual aggression. So every time you acknowledge painful events you are taking responsibility for healing.

Facing Trauma

How does facing trauma without causing harm play a part in taking good care of myself?

_____

_____

Are there traumatic experiences that I have not talked with anyone about?

_____

_____

If so, what will help me to share them with someone I trust?

_____

_____

When do I find the courage and strength to successfully talk about trauma in my life?

_____

_____

What does this prove about using power and control in helpful ways?

_____

_____

How can I use what I have learned about facing trauma to make a successful change in my life?

_____

_____

Staying Clear

Eric was kicked out of class the for daydreaming. When he told a counselor what was happening they realized daydreaming was not the problem. Something in the classroom was triggering Eric to a painful time. He became nervous, drummed excitely on his desk, and disrupted class. Eric did not realize he was doing those things. He was having flashbacks of that scary time. He didn't come out of the flashbacks until the teacher yelled at him. Once Eric figured that out, he and his teacher worked together to reduce triggers that caused the flashbacks. Eric was then able to stay focused on his work.

Once you get in the habit of talking about bad things and not being afraid of them, you can learn to keep your mind clear so that trauma echoes don't confuse you. First of all, you can learn to slow things down a bit. Trauma echoes happen to everyone. They can happen when you least expect them. Sometimes you can predict when they might occur. They may throw you off balance, but you can learn to manage them without causing harm. This means you can control them! They don't have to control you.

Another task that can help you to take good care of yourself is to learn to keep the present clear when you get triggered to past traumas. Keeping the present clear simply means to stay focused on what is going on so that you are aware that the trauma is not happening again. This can take a lot of practice. You can learn ways to keep the present clear so that trauma echoes are not so hard to deal with.

When you figure out what triggers thoughts about bad experiences you can learn to predict when you might have trauma echoes and prepare to manage them in ways that do not cause harm. You can learn to keep the present clear a lot easier when you allow people you trust to help you out. When others know what triggers you they can support you when it happens by talking to you in a soothing way. They can stay with you so that you do not feel alone and isolated or abandoned. They can do things with you, such as take a walk, so that you can stay focused and feel safe.

Top 10
IMPORTANT THINGS ABOUT STAYING CLEAR

_____

_____

_____

_____

_____

_____

_____

_____

Flash backs, bad memories, nightmares and night terrors can make you feel like you are back at the time of the trauma. You may feel helpless and little, like you did when the bad thing happened. You're not! You're a teenager now and have strength and resources to manage pain that you didn't have when it happened. You're bigger, you're smarter, and you know how to ask questions of people you trust so that you can find the answers. You also know how to get away from a bad situation that might cause more bad things to happen.

When you recognize a trauma echo you can manage a flashback, nightmare, or bad memory without losing a sense of where you are. When you have an echo, hold on! When you feel a surge of tension in your body, grab the arm of your chair, a table, the hand of someone you trust, anything close by that is stable. Slow down your breathing as much as you can. Take deep breaths. If you're alone give yourself messages to stay calm. Say nice things to yourself like "I can manage this" "this is old stuff, I can deal with it now" "I can tackle this" "this can be tamed". When you say these things you are giving yourself courage and strength to face the pain.

If someone you trust is with you, think out loud. Say things like "oh no, the bad stuff is back" "here it comes, again" or something like that. Those words will tell others what's going on so that they can support you through it. Share your fears. You might say how scared you are, or how scary it is to remember those things. When you have the courage to share your fear you may become less fearful. See if this works for you.

Staying Clear

How does staying clear play a part in taking good care of myself?

_____

_____

When am I successful in managing trauma echoes without flashbacks or losing sense of where I am?

_____

_____

When I have a trauma echo how do I manage to keep my thoughts clear?

_____

_____

What does this prove about using power and control in helpful ways?

_____

_____

How can I use what I have learned about staying clear to make a successful change in my life?

_____

_____

How is this new information helping me to tame violence and sexual aggression?

_____

_____

Attending to Pain

Attending to pain means accepting pain and facing it at a slow, thoughtful pace. Attending to pain means not making believe that it will go away on it's own. Some pain does not go away on it's own so you have to learn how to manage it in ways that don't cause harm.

Trauma echoes can impact you in a lot of different ways at different times. They can be mild, or vague, recollections; bad memories; or they can be very strong reactions that overwhelm you. Be prepared for all of the feelings and you'll be ready to manage the tough ones. Some feelings you may experience are sadness, fear, confusion, anger, loneliness, terror and rage.

You may start crying, or you might want to scream. Let the tears come! Yell, if you need to! You may feel a lot of energy in your body that makes you want to move around or run. You might feel a strong desire to lash out at someone or something. You might feel like you want to curl up in a ball and hide. These are all normal response to trauma echoes. Let the pain take its course. It will eventually let up. You may not believe that, but it will.

Think about how you can move your body in ways that doesn't hurt you or anyone else. Practice controlling your breathing by slowing it down. After a while your body will slow itself down and you will know that you successfully tackled the pain. Your breathing will return to normal and you may find your body wanting to take some very deep breathes and let out a sigh. The agitation, or nervous energy, will eventually go away, and you will be aware of what's around you. This is a good time to just relax and collect your thoughts.

All human beings need privacy and solitude. Solitude is being alone. It provides an opportunity to reflect and collect your thoughts when no one else is around. Religious people often pray in privacy and solitude. As you learn to control trauma echoes you may find that you want some private time to make sense of what's going on. You can let people know when you need solitude so that they can help you to have some time alone to help the healing process.

There is a difference between being alone and isolation. Isolation means being set apart. Isolation can cause loneliness and confusion. Isolation might bring up fears and trigger trauma echoes about neglect and abandonment. When you are alone you can tell whether the solitude is helping, or hurting. If it's hurting look for someone you trust to talk to and be with. Learning the difference between isolation and solitude is an important part to taking good care of yourself. It can help you to figure out how to successfully respond to trauma echoes in a way that does not cause harm.

It is only though attending to pain, and working through it, that you are able to heal. Running away from it, or raging against it, keep you from taming it. When you address it respectfully you allow it to run its natural course, to flow through your life like a river. When a river is allowed to flow its natural course it serves the purpose of allowing pure water to be a resource to humans, animals and land. When it has served its purpose it joins a lake, or the ocean, and simply becomes a part of all the water on earth. If fallen logs, or rocks damn a river up, problems occur. It might become stagnant, cause a flood or change its course. Things that depend upon water for life might not be able to get it. If bad things contaminate the water it can damage and kill living things. It is important that water remains pure, and that it can flow along a course in order to help keep things alive that depend upon it.

Thinking about pain in this way can help you to make sense of it. When you are clear in your thinking about it you can open yourself up to change. This allows you to make room in you life for dreams and for thinking about becoming the person you want to be.

Attending to Pain

How does attending to pain play a part in taking good care of myself?

_____

When do I successfully attend to my pain without causing harm?

_____

What new things have I learned about attending to my pain?

_____

What does this tell me about my courage, strength and respect for myself?

_____

How can I use this new information to make a successful change in my life?

_____

_____

How will attending to pain without causing harm help me to tame violence and sexual aggression?

_____

_____

Top 10 IMPORTANT
THINGS ABOUT ATTENDING TO PAIN

_____

_____

_____

_____

_____

_____

_____

_____

_____

Ramon suffered beatings from his father until he was seventeen years old. He desperately wanted to be different than his father but he started hitting his girlfriend when she hurt him or made him mad. He realized that arguments with his girlfriend were triggering painful memories of his family. With the help of his counselor he created a safety plan to respond to conflict in new ways. He shared the plan with his family and girlfriend. The next time his father acted like he might hit him Ramon excused himself and ran outside to his bicycle. He took off on his bike so that he could control his nervous energy in solitude. He wanted time to calm down and think about the problem. Ramon reported to his counselor that he rode about thirteen miles and was exhausted when he was done. He said it felt great to get out and have some time alone. Ramon talked about how powerful it felt to get away from his father's abuse and take good care of himself at the same time.

Expressing Genuine feelings

Trauma echoes and the pain they bring up can cause a lot of confusion. Depending on their impact, your body's response can be anywhere from mildly disturbed to overwhelmed. When people are not prepared for them they can be even more difficult to manage. Confusion can cause you to feel mixed up and out of control. Confusion can get in the way of thinking clearly. Confusion caused by painful feelings may have played a part in your decisions to commit acts of violence and sexual aggression. You can change all that! You can learn to figure out the confusion and stop allowing it to cause harm. Learning to figure out painful feelings and to think clearly about them helps you to express your feelings without causing harm.

The more you plan for trauma echoes, and practice managing them, the more successful you can feel in taming them. Making sense of all of the feelings they bring up can help you to gain even more control over them. Having a greater sense of control can help you to feel competent and successful. Learning to identify and accept the whole range of feelings that you have allows you to face pain without fear and a desire to run away from it.

If you're alone when you experience a trauma echo, you may want to write your thoughts down so that you can come back to them as you are making sense of the whole experience. If you are with someone you trust you may want to talk with him or her about the experience. If you don't feel like talking right then, you can make a plan to speak with someone about it later. You may want to rest for a while. Being flooded with emotions can take a lot out of you. Emotions use a lot of energy. Allowing yourself to rest after a powerful emotional experience gives you time to relax and regain some energy. Once you have rested from the initial impact your body is able to return to normal. You may be surprised by how strong you can feel after successfully tackling pain.

When you're ready to make sense of it do so in a safe place with someone you trust. This will give you an opportunity to clear up any confusion, talk about all of the feelings, get some feedback about how you handled it, and plan for continued success in taking good care of yourself.

Expressing Genuine Feelings

How does expressing genuine feelings help me to take good care of myself?

_____

_____

When do I successfully express painful feelings without causing harm?

_____

_____

What does this prove about my courage, strength and respect?

_____

_____

What does it say about using power, control and connection in helpful ways?

_____

_____

How can I use what I have learned about clearly expressing feelings to make a successful change in my life?

_____

_____

How can expressing feelings genuinely help me to tame violence and sexual aggression?

_____

_____

Top10 IMPORTANT THINGS
ABOUT EXPRESSING FEELINGS GENUINELY

_____

_____

_____

_____

_____

_____

_____

_____

_____

_____

Self-Acceptance

An important part of the trauma outcome process is self-acceptance. Self-acceptance is recognizing your own skills and ability to manage challenges in life. Taking good care of yourself results in self-acceptance. It's about developing a belief in yourself that you can handle things. Self-acceptance is not something you get. It is something you practice every day. As you grow up, bad things don't go away, you just learn to handle them better.

When you believe that you can handle a difficult, or painful, situation without causing harm, you build faith in yourself. Faith is unquestioning belief in something. It is complete trust and confidence. Faith takes a lot of practice! When you practice taking good care of yourself every day your faith in yourself grows. You can develop faith in others and they build faith in you. You become stronger and stronger. You learn that you can count on yourself to do good things and you build trust. People trust you and you can learn how to judge when others are trustworthy. You have unlimited opportunities to practice using power and control and connection with others in helpful ways. This is benevolence!

Self-Acceptance

What skills am I using to take good care of myself?

_____

_____

How do these skills help me to build faith in myself and gain
self-acceptance?

_____

_____

What will help me to develop faith in my ability to tame violence and
sexual aggression?

_____

_____

How will this new information help me to use power, control and
connection benevolently?

_____

_____

How can I use what I know about self-acceptance to make a successful
change in my life?

_____

_____

Top 10 IMPORTANT
THINGS ABOUT SELF-ACCEPTANCE

_____

_____

_____

_____

_____

_____

_____

_____

Conclusion

WOW! Have you done a lot of work in this section! Pages and pages of very important questions about healing and learning to take good care of yourself. Taking good care of yourself is a life-long journey. You live in a country that does not value taking good care of yourself. You are constantly getting messages to hurry, hurry, hurry; get with the program; stay on schedule; don't be late! You get messages to eat fast foods that are bad for you. And you get messages to buy, buy, buy, whether, or not, you need something. But you don't get many messages to slow down, to reflect on pain in your life so that you can heal it. You don't get many messages to be thoughtful about whom you can trust so that you can build intimate, safe relationships to attend to the confusion caused by trauma. You don't get much information about how to express feelings so that you can build faith in your abilities to manage them. These are the reasons you have this workbook. So that you can get clear messages about learning to take good care of yourself. Then you can tame the violence and sexual aggression in your life.

Take a few minutes to think creatively about ways that you can continue to practice taking good care of yourself. What messages do you want to give yourself that remind you to slow down? What clear messages about having fun do you want to remember? It may help to remember that some kinds of self-care are better, and more powerful, than others. For example, good nutrition and exercise are better for you in the long run than playing video games and watching television. Talking to friends, and doing things together are much better than hanging around doing nothing and being bored.

Taking Good Care of Myself

How does taking good care of myself play a part in getting into trouble versus staying out of trouble?

_____

_____

When am I successfully taking good care of myself?

_____

_____

What fun things are involved in taking good care of myself ?

_____

_____

What does this prove about using power, control and connection benevolently?

_____

_____

How can I use what I know about taking good care of myself to tame violence and sexual aggression?

_____

_____

You can never think too much about taking good care of yourself. And there are many ways that you can do so. Take some time to think about all of the things that you like to do and how they play a part in taking good care of yourself. Think about your body and your mind and decisions you can make to take good care of your health and well being. Keeping yourself in good working condition can help you to tame violence and sexual aggression and help you to become the person you want to be.

REFLECTIONS ON TAKING GOOD CARE OF MYSELF

How has it been helpful to answer questions about taking good care of myself?

_____

_____

What strengths am I learning about myself?

_____

_____

What challenges am I facing in taking good care of myself?

_____

_____

What will help me prepare to go on to the next section of the workbook?

_____

_____

Top 10 IMPORTANT THINGS
ABOUT TAKING GOOD CARE OF MYSELF

_____

_____

_____

_____

_____

_____

_____

_____

_____

_____

1. Have as much fun as possible

2. Have freedom to do what you want

3. Experience kindness and affection

4. Control your own destiny

5. Use benevolent power

6. Enjoying loving relationships

7. Use your brain thoughtfully

8. Live long and prosper

9. Make the world a better place

10. Allow your spirit to soar!

You receive information all the time that influences decisions about who you want to be. You get a lot of messages that try to tell you what kind of man you should be. Young women get a lot of messages too, they're just different. It's impossible to figure out what kind of person you really want to be when aggressive behavior is controlling your life. Decisions about getting into trouble versus staying out of trouble influence how you become the person you want to be.

When you are able to make sense of your trauma outcome process and learn to control it you have a wonderful opportunity to begin figuring out who you really want to be. This is something that takes your whole life so the sooner you begin the sooner you'll be on your way!

Heroism

Facing pain and accepting genuine emotions that come with it is the most important, and often most scary, part of the healing process. When you have the courage and strength to tackle the depth, and darkness, of such pain you take on a Herculean task. Hercules was a mythical person known to be very powerful and courageous. A Herculean task is one that is very difficult and requires great strength. When a Herculean task is successfully completed a person can become a hero. A hero is any person admired for his, or her, qualities,

_____

_____

_____

_____

_____

_____

_____

_____

chapter seven: Becoming the Person I Want to Be

or achievements, and regarded as an ideal or model. Anyone who is able to face the darkness and despair of painful life experiences without hurting anyone is a true hero.

Every man who is able to cry when he feels intense pain may be facing a Herculean task. Since boys are taught that tears are bad, and a sign of weakness, it is very hard for many young men to believe the opposite. Some young men are afraid that if they start crying they will never stop. Tears usually last a short time. As pain goes away so do the tears.

Tears are extremely important in the healing process. Tears are a body's way of releasing pain. There's nothing shameful about them. They are simply part of a body's function. When tear ducts don't work properly it causes problems and requires medical attention. Everyone's body experiences a lot of pain in a lifetime and crying in response to that pain helps it to heal faster and more completely. We should never miss a good opportunity to cry!

Because our society does not know how important this effort is you might find that you are an unsung hero. An unsung hero is one whose courage and strength may not be celebrated. There are a lot of unsung heroes in our world. I hope that your courage to face your pain in ways that do not cause harm to yourself or others is honored and celebrated by people who care about you. I commend you! Whenever you attend to your pain in this way you are taking excellent care of yourself.

Heroism

How does heroism play a part in staying out of trouble?

_____

_____

What helps me to face a Herculean task?

_____

_____

When am I being heroic?

_____

_____

Who comes to mind when I think of a heroic person?

_____

_____

How do they show their heroism?

_____

_____

How can I use what I have learned about heroism to make a successful change in my life?

_____

_____

How can heroism help me to become the person I want to be?

_____

_____

Empathy and Compassion

Empathy is the ability to share in another's emotions or feelings. When you are able to understand the full impact that violence and sexual aggression has on victims, including yourself, you are able to consider true empathy. Empathy can help you to understand how pain in life influences thoughts and actions.

When you are able to understand empathy, or walk in your victim's shoes, it can become a powerful tool in taming violence and sexual aggression. Thinking of others allows people to consider benevolence and compassion. *Compassion is sorrow for the sufferings or trouble of another, accompanied by an urge to help.* When you connect the way you felt when bad things happened to you with your victims, you can think differently about how you want to behave.

A lot of healing starts with helping others. You might find that you want to help yourself first. It doesn't matter where you start. It just matters that you start. Developing empathy and compassion for yourself will help you to consider practicing empathy and compassion for others.

What was it that you really needed when bad things were happening to you? I'll bet you needed love, and to be cared for. A hug and comforting words help people to heal from bad experiences. Everyone needs to know that there are people you can go to when times are tough. Everyone needs comfort and compassion. A hand to hold and someone to talk to are some of the best gifts in life. Empathy and compassion lead to benevolence.

Demitri was treated poorly in school and his community. His father had physically abused him and his mother treated him disrespectfully. Demitri's pain, confusion and frustration influenced getting into trouble and he was arrested for his crimes. At first he acted like a tough guy but he took a stand for himself and expressed his pain and humiliation.

Demitri faced a Herculean task in telling his mother and stepfather how badly he felt about the way they treated him. His mother saw that Demitri was right. A court order prevented Demitri from having contact with the victim of his crime. He wrote a letter of apology and explained his crime to a judge who shared the letter with his victim. Demitri realized that he hurt his victim in much the same way he had been hurt. He connected those feelings with his own humiliation and realize how awful it was for his victim.

Demitri changed a lot in treatment. He worked hard to tame his violence and sexual aggression. He made plans for work and independent living. He talked about learning to treat friends with respect and care.

Empathy and Compassion

How do empathy and compassion play a part in staying out of trouble?

_____

When am I treated with empathy and compassion?

_____

How do empathy and compassion comfort me?

_____

When do I show empathy and compassion?

_____

What does that prove about my desire to use power, control and connection in helpful ways?

_____

How can this new information help me to tame violence and sexual aggression?

_____

How can I use what I know about empathy and compassion to become the person I want to be?

_____

Top 10 IMPORTANT
THINGS ABOUT EMPATHY AND COMPASSION

_____

_____

_____

_____

_____

_____

_____

_____

Making Amends

To make amends is to do something to make up for injury, loss, or damage that someone has caused. Taming violence and sexual aggression involves making amends. It can help you, your victims, and anyone affected by your crimes, to get on with life and heal the pain. Making amends is a heroic effort to take a stand against violence and sexual aggression. Honorable acts come from empathy and compassion. Making amends reflect your success in overcoming pain and anger. It shows that you want to become a person who is admired by others.

Making amends happens in a variety of different ways. The most powerful way to make amends is to take full responsibility for causing any pain and to apologize to anyone who was hurt by acts of violence or sexual aggression. This takes a lot of courage! Apologizing is an act of great honor!

Making Amends

How does making amends play a part in staying out of trouble?

_____

When do I have the courage to make amends?

_____

How can it help my victims to heal?

_____

How does it help me to heal?

_____

What does making amends tell me about my use of power, control and connection?

_____

How can I use what I know about making amends to make a successful change in my life?

_____

How is having the strength, courage and honor to make amends helping me to become the person I want to be?

_____

Top 10 IMPORTANT
THINGS ABOUT MAKING AMENDS

_____

_____

_____

_____

_____

_____

_____

_____

Forgiveness

To forgive is give up resentment or the desire to punish. It is an ability to let go of anger. Deciding to forgive can influence getting into trouble versus staying out of trouble. Just like all of the other things you have addressed in this workbook, forgiveness takes practice. You might think that forgiveness is a Herculean task. Sometimes it is. It can be very hard to forgive someone who has hurt you deeply.

Some people say you should forgive and forget. I don't believe that is possible. Trauma is seldom forgotten. I think that you simply learn to live with the memory of trauma in your life. When you are strong and courageous you work hard to prevent the memories from causing any harm. This is the decision to tame violence and sexual aggression.

There is an old saying that "to err is human, to forgive is divine". What a powerful statement! Everybody makes mistakes, but it takes greatness to be able to forgive. Wow! This is one tall order! How do you learn to rise above pain to forgive those who have hurt you? How do the people you have hurt, rise above their pain, to forgive you? You can figure this out and go on to become the person you want to be.

Many bad things that happen in life are no one's fault. Forgiveness comes easier when no one is at fault. When someone you love dies it is extremely painful. If you are afraid to feel the intense pain of such a loss you might try to hide it by acting angry with the doctors or nurses who couldn't keep that person alive. When you are able to face the pain you realize that death is not usually anyone's fault. As you let go of the desire to punish the medical staff, the anger goes away and you are able to forgive them for not being able to save your loved one.

If you believe in God, you may be angry that God took your loved one away from you. Sometimes people in pain blame God and have to take some time to figure out how they will practice forgiveness. If you feel badly about something you did you might be blaming yourself, and turning your anger inward against yourself. Sharing such thoughts with someone you trust can help you learn to forgive yourself.

Some bad things that happen may be the fault of someone who mistreated you. It may be difficult to consider forgiving them. If they are sorry for what they have done, apologize, and make amends, it might be easier to forgive them. It still takes some work. It can take a long time to forgive people who hurt you.

Unfortunately in life many people who hurt others, and cause trauma, don't apologize or receive punishment for their crimes. When people who hurt you have not made amends it can play a part in your struggle with getting into trouble versus staying out of trouble. It may feel very unfair that you are paying for the violent, or sexually aggressive crimes that you committed while people who may have hurt you in similar ways have not had to pay for their crimes. When people who hurt you don't make amends it can be harder to heal the pain. Life is very unfair at times. Just because life is so unfair does not mean that it is okay to commit criminal acts, even when others get away with them.

It can be really hard to even consider forgiving those people! It also makes sense that the pain you felt from being hurt by them got worse from anger and resentment that grew from knowing that they were not held accountable for their bad behavior. That's a lot of righteous anger! Righteous means having a legitimate right to something. In this case it means that you have a right to be angry about such injustice.

So how do you learn to practice forgiveness when you have had such awful experiences? This can be a tough one!

Forgiveness

How does forgiveness play a part in staying out of trouble?

_____

What things that happened to me have I not forgiven others for?

_____

What is preventing me from forgiving them?

_____

When am I able to forgive?

_____

What things do I want to be forgiven for?

_____

Who do I want to forgive me?

_____

What do I need to do to earn their forgiveness?

_____

_____

How is this new information helping me to take a stand for courage, strength and respect?

_____

What does this prove about using power benevolently?

_____

How can I use what I know about forgiveness to make a successful change in my life?

_____

How can forgiveness play a part in helping me become the person I want to be?

_____

_____

Top 10
IMPORTANT THINGS ABOUT FORGIVENESS

Honor and Integrity

Healing continues when you learn how to face up to pain, and tackle it. When you stop causing pain to yourself and others you can think about yourself differently. You may be surprised to develop a high regard that is called "honor". Honor is about giving respect, earning a good reputation and having a strong sense of what is right and what is wrong. It is about daring to take a stand for yourself to stay out of trouble. Integrity is a big word that comes from acting with honor. When you practice taking good care of yourself you are acting with honor and integrity. People look up to you, respect you and admire you. You learn to respect and honor yourself. You can stand tall instead of cowering and running away from problems and the pain that they cause. You no longer need to bully others in order to feel powerful and in control. You can stop lying and cheating because you know that destructive behavior is not in your self-interest.

When you embrace honor and integrity you can decide what kind of person you want to be, and you can become that person! You can learn to make decisions, and choices, based upon your desire to do good rather than harm.

One way to stay out of trouble is to figure out what kind of person you want to be and stay focused on that goal. All of the effort that you have put into this workbook so far can help you do this. Becoming the person you want to be is a process based upon everything you think and do. It is a daily challenge to behave in ways that help you to feel good about life and living.

Demitri decided that he wanted to become an honest man who would work to pay for his own apartment and food. He wanted to learn how to date girls and he hoped to fall in love and have a family. Soon after he left residential treatment he got a job and continues to work full time. He paid his legal fines and saved his money to move out of his mother's house.

Top 10 IMPORTANT THINGS ABOUT BECOMING THE PERSON I WANT TO BE

_____

_____

_____

_____

_____

_____

_____

_____

_____

Honor and Integrity

How do honor and integrity play a part in staying out of trouble?

_____

_____

When do I behave with honor and integrity?

_____

_____

What does this prove about me as a person?

_____

_____

How can I use what I know about honor and integrity to make a successful change in my life?

_____

_____

How are honor and integrity helping me to tame violence and sexual aggression?

_____

_____

What part do honor and integrity play in helping me to become the person I want to be?

_____

_____

What Kind of Person Do I Want to Be?

What qualities come to mind when I think of the type of person I want to be?

_____

_____

What types of things do I want to do?

_____

_____

How do I want interact with others?

_____

_____

When am I successfully being the person I want to be?

_____

_____

What does this prove about using power, control and connection in benevolent ways?

_____

_____

How can I use what I know about becoming the person I want to be to make a successful change in my life?

_____

_____

How is this new information helping me to tame violence and sexual aggression?

_____

_____

REFLECTIONS ON BECOMING THE PERSON I WANT TO BE

How is it helpful to figure out what kind of person I want to be?

_____

_____

What have I learned about myself from these questions?

_____

_____

How am I daring to take a stand to become the person I want to be?

_____

_____

What will help me prepare to go on to the next section of the
workbook?

_____

_____

Conclusion

You are almost there! You have done incredible work in making sense of your life and thinking about the future that you want to create for yourself. You are learning how to become the master of your destiny! Destiny is what will happen in the future. To master something is to rule or govern, to become an expert in. To become a master of your destiny is to be clear about what you want out of life so that you can control and govern the direction you take to get there.

Earlier in the workbook you answered some questions about your dreams. All human beings have dreams. Not everyone has the courage and strength to pursue those dreams and make them a reality. Not all dreams will come true but a wise man, named Elbert Hubbard, once said "there is no failure except in no longer trying".

The reason you had the questions about dreams early on in the workbook was to help you think about things that might help you to tame violence and sexual aggression. Dreams can have a very strong influence on your life. When you create dreams that reflect your hopes and desires, and hold on to them, you are much more likely to make them come true. Being clear about your dreams can help you to prepare for the opportunity to pursue them. Telling people you trust about your dreams can help them to support your efforts and help make your dreams come true.

Taming violence and sexual aggression can help you pursue dreams that you would not have been able to before. You can dare to take a stand for yourself and stop committing crimes. You can learn to spend time making your dreams come true. There is nothing more fun than living the life you really want to live. When you decide to pursue your dreams it can be helpful to make a list of them.

Dreams I Have About ...

having fun?

_____

_____

talents I want to develop?

_____

_____

loving relationships?

_____

_____

taking good care of myself?

_____

_____

becoming the person I want to be?

_____

_____

Now that you have thought some more about dreams, please go back to the section in this workbook on dreams. They are on page 9. Take a look at your answers then come back to this page.

Some dreams come easy and some dreams take a long time to realize. Here are some more activities to help you prepare to pursue your dreams.

chapter eight: Pursuing Your Dreams

Pursuing My Dreams

How have any of my dreams changed since beginning this workbook?

_____

_____

What new dreams have I created?

_____

_____

What do these new dreams tell me about how I can use power, control and connection to tame violence and sexual aggression?

_____

_____

What does this prove about my courage, strength and respect?

_____

_____

How has answering all of these questions helped me to be more clear about my dreams?

_____

_____

How will my dreams help me to become the person I want to be?

_____

_____

How will becoming the person I want to be help me to pursue these dreams?

_____

_____

Top 10
IMPORTANT THINGS ABOUT MY DREAMS

_____

_____

_____

_____

_____

_____

_____

_____

Now, think about these dreams and place them in the order in which you might pursue them.

THE ORDER IN WHICH I CAN PURSUE THESE DREAMS

1. _____

2. _____

3. _____

4. _____

5. _____

6. _____

7. _____

8. _____

9. _____

10. _____

Dream Number **ONE**:

What do I want, and need, to make this dream a reality?

_____

How long do I think it will take to make this dream come true?

_____

How will it help me to become the person I want to be?

_____

How will it support my lifetime effort to tame violence and sexual aggression?

_____

Dream Number **TWO**:

What do I want, and need, to make this dream a reality?

_____

How long do I think it will take to make this dream come true?

_____

How will it help me to become the person I want to be?

_____

How will it support my lifetime effort to tame violence and sexual aggression?

_____

Dream Number **THREE**:

What do I want, and need, to make this dream a reality?

_____

How long do I think it will take to make this dream come true?

_____

How will it help me to become the person I want to be?

_____

How will it support my lifetime effort to tame violence and sexual aggression?

_____

Dream Number **FOUR**:

What do I want, and need, to make this dream a reality?

_____

How long do I think it will take to make this dream come true?

_____

How will it help me to become the person I want to be?

_____

How will it support my lifetime effort to tame violence and sexual aggression?

_____

Dream Number **FIVE**:

What do I want, and need, to make this dream a reality?

_____

How long do I think it will take to make this dream come true?

_____

How will it help me to become the person I want to be?

_____

How will it support my lifetime effort to tame violence and sexual aggression?

_____

Dream Number **SIX**:

What do I want, and need, to make this dream a reality?

_____

How long do I think it will take to make this dream come true?

_____

How will it help me to become the person I want to be?

_____

How will it support my lifetime effort to tame violence and sexual aggression?

_____

Dream Number **SEVEN**:

What do I want, and need, to make this dream a reality?

_____

How long do I think it will take to make this dream come true?

_____

How will it help me to become the person I want to be?

_____

How will it support my lifetime effort to tame violence and sexual aggression?

_____

Dream Number **EIGHT**:

What do I want, and need, to make this dream a reality?

_____

How long do I think it will take to make this dream come true?

_____

How will it help me to become the person I want to be?

_____

How will it support my lifetime effort to tame violence and sexual aggression?

_____

Dream Number **NINE**:

What do I want, and need, to make this dream a reality?

_____

How long do I think it will take to make this dream come true?

_____

How will it help me to become the person I want to be?

_____

How will it support my lifetime effort to tame violence and sexual aggression?

_____

Dream Number **TEN**:

What do I want, and need, to make this dream a reality?

_____

How long do I think it will take to make this dream come true?

_____

How will it help me to become the person I want to be?

_____

How will it support my lifetime effort to tame violence and sexual aggression?

_____

Conclusion

When you are finished with this workbook you will be challenged to practice all of the things that you have learned for the rest of your life This is the same challenge that all human beings have. Being a person of honor requires constant practice. Pursuing your dreams takes courage and persistence. *Persistence means continuing over a long period of time.* Persistence in managing pain in ways that no longer cause harm can help you to think about your life differently.

Using the trauma outcome process to tame violence and sexual aggression is a tool that you can use to help you through difficult times for the rest of your life. It helps everyone to understand patterns of destructive behavior that cause problems in life. You have done remarkable work in completing this exploration of your life. Your strength, courage and respect have helped you complete a Herculean task!

You have covered a lot of ground in this workbook. You've spent a lot of time thinking about things like strength and courage and respect. You've thought about how others treat you and how you treat others. You've explored a lot of questions about power and control and connection. You've had a lot of opportunities to figure out pain in your life and to make decisions about healing that pain.

Connection is perhaps the most powerful force in the universe. All of the elements of nature are connected in very complex ways and work together to maintain balance for growth. You are part of this process. You now have the opportunity to go forward and continue to practice all of the things that you have learned from this effort. Successful people rely on the goodness and support of other trustworthy people. It is important that you always have people like this in your life. You can't do it alone.

REFLECTIONS ON PURSUING MY DREAMS

How has it been helpful to answer questions about pursing my
dreams?

_____

_____

Who has helped me the most with this effort?

_____

_____

How will I stay connected to them in the future?

_____

_____

How can we plan for and schedule this ongoing connection?

_____

_____

What have I learned about myself that will keep me from committing
any acts of violence or sexual aggression?

_____

_____

What will help me to plan for continued success?

_____

_____

Sometimes there are people in your life, with whom you have a connection that is not in your best interest. There might be people you have been close to who have influenced your decisions to act in violent or sexually aggressive ways. These people are not trustworthy. Unless they have made a significant change in their life to stop destructive behavior it may not be safe to continue your connection with them. These kinds of people place you at risk for returning to a life of crime. Even though you may love these people you may have to decide to protect yourself from their influence. This can be hard, but you can do it. You can learn to love them from afar. You can continue to love them while knowing that it's not safe to be around them. It is sad when you have to do this, but it is much better than hurting others and spending time in jail.

It is very important to realize that there are other people who will love you. Their names and addresses are on this page. Keep this page, or a copy of it with you so that you can contact them whenever the going gets tough. Stay connected with these people. They will be there for you. And you can be there for them.

Leon committed crimes that landed him in a maximum secure placement. He had a tough time in treatment but he stuck with it and successfully tamed violence and sexual aggression. While he was there he thought a lot about all the people who helped him succeed. His mother supported him and her minister helped her a lot. Leon's probation officer met with him once a month and a few staff helped him a lot. His high school football coach and a history teacher he liked stayed in contact with him.

When it was time for Leon to go home he organized a meeting with all of those people. They talked about how each of them would support Leon's plan for continued success. They planned time to connect with Leon in the future so that he would feel support as he pursued his dreams.

PEOPLE I CAN TRUST TO SUPPORT MY SUCCESS

Name: _____ Phone Number: _____

Name: _____ Phone Number: _____

Name: _____ Phone Number: _____

Name: _____ Phone Number: _____

Name: _____ Phone Number: _____

Top 10 IMPORTANT THINGS ABOUT TAMING
VIOLENCE AND/OR SEXUAL AGGRESSION

_____

_____

_____

_____

_____

_____

_____

_____

Of all the work that you have done in treatment which parts of this work book do you think will help you the most? Please take some time to write these things down so that they will stay with you and continue to help you along your life's journey. Make sure you share them with the people you trust so that they can continue to support your success.

Go thoughtfully and carefully on your life's journey.

You must be the change you wish to see in the world.

Mahatma Gandhi

Reference List for Service Providers

Araji, S. (1997). *Sexually Aggressive Children.* Thousand Oaks: Sage Publications.

Arnow, J. (1995). *Teaching Peace.* New York: Perigree Press.

Burn, S. (1996). *The Social Psychology of Gender.* New York: McGraw-Hill, Inc.

Burton, J., Rasmussen, L., Bradshaw, J. Christopherson, B., and Huke, S. (1998). *Treating children with sexually abusive behavior problems.* New York: The Haworth Maltreatment and Trauma Press.

Durrant, M. (1993). *Residential Treatment.* New York: W.W.Norton & Company.

Garbarino, J. (1999). *Lost Boys.* New York: The Free Press.

Garbarino, J. (1995) *Raising Children in a Socially Toxic Environment.* San Francisco: Jossey-Bass Publishers.

Gray, A. (1989). *New Concepts in Sexual Abuse Recovery:* Healing the Effects of Trauma. Paper presented at the Fourth Annual Training Conference on the Treatment of Juvenile Sex Offenders, Salt Lake City, Utah.

Hermann, J. (1992). *Trauma and Recovery.* New York: Basic Books.

His Holiness the Dalai Lama. (2000). *Ethics for a New Millennium.* New York: Riverhead Books.

Jenkins, A. (1991). *Invitations to Responsibility: The Therapeutic Engagement of Men Who are Violent and Abusive.* Adelaide, South Australia: Dulwich Centre Publications.

Middleton-Moz, J. (1999). *Boiling Point: The High Cost of Unhealthy Anger to Individuals and Society.* Deerfield Beach, Florida: Health Communication, Inc.

Miller, S., Duncan, B. & Hubble, M. (1997). *Escape From Babel: Toward a Unifying Language for Psychotherapy Practice.* New York: W.W. Norton & Company

Pollack, W. (2000). *Real Boys' Voices.* New York: Random House.

Pollack, W. (1998). *Real Boys.* New York: Henry Holt and Company.

Rasmussen, L., Burton, J., and Christopherson, B. (1992). *Precursors to Offending and the Trauma Outcome Process in Sexually Reactive Children.* Journal of child Sexual Abuse, 1 (1), 33-48.

Real, T. (1997). *I Don't Want to Talk About It.* New York: Fireside, Simon & Shuster.

Ryan, G. & Lane, S. (1997). *Juvenile Sexual Offending.* San Francisco: Jossey-Bass.

White, M., and Epston, D. (1990). *Narrative Means to Therapeutic Ends.* New York: W.W. Norton & Company.